Counselling Skills
for Professional Helpers

Gateways to Counselling

Consultant editor:
Windy Dryden, Professor of Counselling at Goldsmiths
College, University of London

Series editor:
Maria Stasiak

Project manager:
Carron Staplehurst

The *Gateways to Counselling* series comprises books on various aspects of counselling theory and practice. Written with the assistance of the Central School of Counselling and Therapy, one of the largest counselling training organisations in the UK, the books address the needs of both students and tutors and are relevant for a range of training courses, regardless of specific orientation.

Other books in the series include:

STARVING TO LIVE
The paradox of anorexia nervosa
Alessandra Lemma-Wright

AN INTRODUCTION TO CO-DEPENDENCY FOR
COUNSELLORS
Gill Reeve

COUNSELLING IN A GENERAL PRACTICE SETTING
James Breese

ON LISTENING AND LEARNING
Student counselling in further and higher education
Colin Lago and Geraldine Shipton

TRANSCULTURAL COUNSELLING
Zack Eleftheriadou

COUNSELLING SKILLS FOR PROFESSIONAL HELPERS

John Pratt

Central Book Publishing Ltd
London

First published 1994
by Central Book Publishing Ltd
80 Paul Street
London EC2A 4NE

Reprinted 1997
© 1994 John Pratt

Typeset in 10 on 12 point Century Roman and Optima by
Intype, London
Printed in Great Britain by
Tudor Printing, Park Road, Barnet

Cover illustration by Helen S. Roper

British Library Cataloguing in Publication Data
Pratt, John
Counselling Skills for Professional
Helpers. – (Gateways to Counselling
Series)
I. Title   II. Series
361.323
ISBN 1–898458–00–6

Contents

Introduction

Many thousands of people in this country provide a 'helping' service for others. Hundreds, perhaps a few thousand of these are called 'counsellors'. Among the vast numbers who are not so designated are many who regularly and purposefully use counselling skills with their clients. It is to these professional helpers that this book is addressed.

The book is intended to offer a guide to some areas of counselling experience that are judged to be both central and useful for the professional helper. It deals with the use of skills, the theory underpinning those skills and the self-awareness necessary to free the helper to work in the client's best interests. Importantly, too, it maps out the management of the counselling skills process and the helper's own development in the counselling role.

Thus in Chapter 1 the nature of counselling in general and counselling skills in particular is explored. Chapter 2 describes the basic skills of the counselling skills approach, puts these into the context of professional helping and illustrates their use. The theoretical attitudes that support the counselling skills approach are discussed in Chapter 4, while Chapter 5 explains the significance of self-awareness in the counselling skills relationship, indicating the importance of this for helpers who use 'self as instrument' in their work. Chapter 6 deals with the many contextual factors affecting the use of counselling skills – especially the role conflict inherent in professional helping where counselling is not explicitly recognised as such. Chapter 6 also considers the management of the counselling skills process – giving time, offering help, beginning and ending, etc. Finally Chapter 7 examines possible means of

development for the counselling skills user, discussing training, supervision and other sources of learning.

Professional helpers are more often women than men. For
this reason I have arbitrarily called the helper 'she' throughout
the book in contrast to any general reference to the client as
'he'. Similarly the examples refer mainly to women in the
counselling role. The word 'helper' has itself been brought into
question recently as implying some kind of political advantage
which prejudices the identity of the client who 'has to be
helped'. Whilst acknowledging this and the fact that the term
'worker', providing a 'service', goes some way to avoiding the
problem I still prefer 'helper' both for its clarity and its wide
recognition. Again, 'client' is preferred for the most generally
suitable term for the 'helpee' role, though it is accepted that
many professions have other more specific terms such as
'patient', 'resident', 'student', 'relative' and so on.

Much of what I have written owes something to the many
groups of professional helpers that I have worked with,
especially at Castle Priory at Wallingford. I have learnt from
them of the special relationships they have with their clients
and of their difficulties in taking on the counselling role. As
one of three men in my parental family I would also like to
acknowledge the learning and understanding I have had from
the four women of my own family, that is from my wife, Jean
and from my daughters, Noelle, Jacqueline and Suzanne.

1

What are Counselling Skills?

WHO ARE COUNSELLING SKILLS FOR?

Jan was a district nurse who opted to take a six-day course entitled 'An Introduction to Counselling Skills'. She was professionally competent, built good relationships with her patients and frequently needed to 'counsel' them on issues arising from the illness or condition she was treating, whether these issues were about caring for the patient at home, family responsibilities and relationships, financial difficulties, impending loss or simply to do with getting more support.

Before the course Jan believed she already knew what 'counselling' was, and although in practice she sometimes found the going a bit tough and had suspicions that there were aspects of counselling she needed to know more about, she was basically attending the course to brush up her skills and to confirm that she was on the right track.

On the first day of the course, however, it became clear that counselling was different in some respects from what she and others on the course had supposed, even assumed, it was in their working practice. In the initial workshop and discussion it became clear that giving advice and information were, at best, very low priorities when using counselling skills. Also, and contrary to Jan's actual experience hitherto, finding 'answers' or even ways forward in the troublesome situation she and her patient were discussing were seen to be much more the responsibility of the patient than herself. In fact it seemed very much as though she needed to put most of her previous learning to one side and to begin simply by listening longer and more carefully to her patient than she had done before.

So what then had she come to learn? What was the course about? What does the term 'counselling skills' mean in the context of the practice of a professional helper who is not actually employed as a counsellor; for someone like herself, or a health visitor; for a physiotherapist, an occupational therapist or a doctor; for a residential care worker, a social worker or a teacher? For these and many other groups of workers, particularly managers and those who have a personnel or training function in industrial and service organisations, the use of counselling skills has become increasingly common practice in recent years. However, these people are not actually called 'counsellors' and the activity of counselling may not be part of their job description. Yet in the course of their work they meet others whom they find can be helped by the use of counselling skills. The 'others' may be labelled patients, clients, relatives, students, employees, colleagues or even bosses! Counselling skills have a wide application in principle but their discriminating and careful use is part of the process of learning in the counselling field.

WHAT IS THE PURPOSE OF COUNSELLING SKILLS?

One of Jan's patients is Penny. She has had multiple sclerosis for fifteen years and is now bed-ridden at home where she is looked after by her husband, Eric. Penny is now 52 and is almost totally dependent on Eric though she tries to do as much as she can. Eric is able to provide most of the care she needs since he retired from work two years ago. He has always been anxious to do what is best for Penny, and Jan has been involved in the provision of several different kinds of practical help, including occasional relief from his role as Penny's carer.

On the last visit, Eric managed to speak to Jan as she was leaving. He told her that he was feeling very tense about the situation at home and that he didn't think he would be able to go on with it much longer. There were no obvious ways of offering more practical help to Eric and in any case it may not be that he was asking for this. Jan went back into the house and sat down with Eric in a place where they could talk privately . . .

Now Jan is able to respond to Eric's needs by giving him the time and opportunity to tell her about himself and how he feels. Her use of counselling skills could enable several useful things to happen:

1 Eric identifies what his worries or concerns are;
2 Jan shows Eric that she understands him and how he feels;
3 Jan can decide what kind of further response to make;
4 Eric feels less burdened for having explained his worries, perhaps seeing them in a different perspective as a result of doing so.

This illustrates some of the uses of counselling skills. In working with clients, helpers use counselling skills in much the same way as counsellors use counselling. It is therefore relevant to consider what counselling as a generic activity sets out to achieve. Three general definitions of counselling which are significant in revealing similar purposes to counselling skills are:

1 '(a service consisting of) helping people to adjust or or deal with personal problems, etc. by enabling them to discover for themselves the solution to the problems while receiving sympathetic attention from the counsellor.'

(Chambers English Dictionary)

Here, the word 'solution' is probably less fitting than the ideas of adjustment to and dealing with personal problems. Many of the difficulties that people choose to talk about – and the various kinds of loss are typical of these – do not have solutions in the sense of 'finding the answer' and it could be misleading to pretend that they do. However, it is reassuring to see this kind of definition actually appearing in a dictionary, this itself being the result of a persistent effort by the British Association for Counselling (BAC) for such representation. The next definition of counselling is one which the BAC has itself proposed:

2 'Counselling is a process through which one person helps another by purposeful conversation in a supportive and understanding atmosphere. It tries to establish an open and trustful relationship in which the client can express his thoughts and feelings in such a way as to clarify the situation he is in, come to terms with some new experience,

realize his assets and potential in dealing with a difficulty, face the problem more objectively and with less anxiety or tension. Counselling facilitates these actions and thus enables the client to make his own decisions from the possibilities he sees available to him.'

(British Association for Counselling 1969)

This is a much more comprehensive definition, referring to the attitude of the participants, the atmosphere in which they work, the relationship they establish as well as some of the processes involved. Above all, it implicitly values the autonomy of the client in dealing with his difficulties. The third definition of counselling emphasises the client's own awareness and decision-making and is offered by Barrie Hopson of Life-skills Associates, who puts counselling at one end of a continuum of helper activities scaled according to the 'authority' of the helper.

3(a) *Counselling*: helping someone explore a problem so that he can decide what to do about it (for example, to talk about a person's loss of self-worth after their partner has left them).

(b) *Teaching*: helping someone acquire knowledge and skills that you have and they don't (for example, to read, to play cards or to drive a car).

(c) *Giving advice*: making suggestions about a course of action another person can and possibly should take, looking at it from your position (for example, providing legal advice, telling a friend what to do).

(d) *Direct action*: taking action yourself to provide for someone else's needs (for example, bathing a baby, feeding a helpless patient).

The first of these, (a), again reflects the essential characteristics of the other definitions of counselling, all of which imply that it is essentially an *enabling* activity in which the client may express, explore, discover, clarify and come to terms with his own experience and feelings, consequently taking decisions and actions in accordance with these. Although the use of counselling skills is not counselling but part of another professional role it nevertheless shares the essence of these defi-

4

nitions in their attempts to convey both the intention and method of counselling.

WHEN AND WHERE ARE COUNSELLING SKILLS USED?

For persons who call themselves 'counsellors', the 'where' and 'when' of their counselling is relatively straightforward. Counselling may take place at an office, consulting room or in any other private space established for the purpose by the organisation, agency or counselling body. The wide and still growing range of settings in which such formal counselling occurs is well documented in, for example, the *Handbook of Counselling in Britain* (Dryden *et al*. 1989) and includes school and higher education, medical contexts, social work and, of course, a number of agencies specifically created and maintained to offer counselling services.

Counselling skills, on the other hand, may be offered in diverse and often impromptu locations, perhaps hastily adapted and frequently unsuitable for the counselling transaction. When the would-be counsellor looks for a place near to hand that is private, quiet and free from interruptions via door or phone she is probably out of luck. Counselling skills may have to be used in bedrooms, bathrooms, corridors, waiting rooms, wards and workshops, or in corners just out of earshot of those working or living nearby. The intimacy of the pre-arranged helping or working situation may have created the opportunity for a person to confide. Hence the nurse hears a very personal statement when she is bathing her patient; the occupational health nurse when she is in her office perhaps listening to a staff member describing symptoms; the physiotherapist in a cubicle giving a treatment; the foreman in the canteen over a tea break; and so on.

This is one of a number of practical problems that present themselves to the users of counselling skills. Another is the management of time. This, of course, may be difficult even for the designated counsellor, despite the fact that appointments and session lengths are usually contracted beforehand. In using counselling skills the helper may have to ask herself questions like: how important is this? How much time can I give to it now? Could/should this be postponed to a later time or date? How often can I make time to work with this person?

How much time is he or she expecting from me? Should my (counselling) response be offered on a more formal and perhaps explicit basis at another time and place?

At this point it is sufficient to identify these as important issues in the use of counselling skills. In Chapter 5 these and other contextual factors will be looked at in more detail and some management principles and practice offered.

COUNSELLING SKILLS AND COUNSELLING AS A PROFESSIONAL PRACTICE

In what has been said so far differences between those who use counselling skills and those who practise as counsellors have been implied rather than made explicit. Again, this is an important issue and one that has been examined by the British Association for Counselling and others. For example, in a recent report of the Lead Body on Advice, Guidance and Counselling (funded by the Employment Department), counselling is defined:

[as] 'an activity freely entered into by the person seeking help' it offers the opportunity to identify things for the client themselves that are troubling or perplexing. It is clearly and explicitly contracted, and the boundaries of the relationship identified. The activity itself is designed to help self-exploration and understanding. The process should help to identify thoughts, emotions and behaviours that once accessed, may offer the client opportunities for a greater sense of personal resources and self-determined change.

In contrast, counselling skills are defined as:

high-level communication, interpersonal and social skills used intentionally in a manner consistent with the goals and values of counselling ethics. The principled use of these skills facilitates the client's purpose and enhances personal understanding of themselves and/or their situations. As a direct result of using counselling skills the professional role of the user will be enhanced.

(Russell *et al*. 1992)

The implication here is that the 'professional role of the user' is not that of 'counsellor'. What is not addressed explicitly in the latter definition is the same seeking of a contracted and boundaried relationship which is so important in counselling. This we will consider in Chapter 5. Finally, useful pluralistic definitions of counselling and counselling skills appear in Barbara Pearce's chapter, 'Counselling skills in the context of professional and organizational growth', in the *Handbook of Counselling in Britain* (Dryden *et al.* 1989: 184ff.). She refers first to counselling as a generic helping strategy, distinguishable from other strategies such as teaching, giving advice or information in much the same way as does Barrie Hopson, above. She refers secondly to counselling as a professional practice, using a range of specific therapeutic approaches, such as Transactional Analysis or Gestalt therapy. Counselling skills, she argues, are common to both and form the basis of counselling practice. Finally she describes a 'counselling-skills movement' comprising 'people who use counselling skills consciously and who have had some training but who are not professional counsellors'. This latter concept is partly role-based and corresponds largely to the intentions of this book which aims to inform the thinking and practice of the many professionals who practise counselling, but who do not normally call themselves counsellors. We too shall use the term 'counselling skills' to refer to an integrated attitude and approach taken by non-counsellor helpers who see this as an appropriate way of responding to their clients and in doing so differentiate counselling skills from their other means of helping. Counselling skills, as defining an approach, should not be confused with the actual behavioural skills of the counselling skills user, as described for example in Chapter 2. These will be referred to as the 'basic skills of counselling', and this implies such activities as paraphrasing, summarising, etc.

COUNSELLING AS SKILLED BEHAVIOUR

Skill is a topic which has received a great deal of attention in the psychological literature, dating from as far back as World War II. Most of the interest has been in three areas – physical skills as used in sport or work (such as catching a ball or typing), intellectual and mental skills (such as reading or mental arithmetic) and social skills such as giving and receiving information, presenting oneself to others, maintaining a conversation and so on. Social skills and skilled performances, such as interviewing, selling or counselling, have several important elements. They refer to some aim, like trying to sell a car, provide help or select a suitable person for a job. In pursuit of this aim they rely upon both an accurate perception of others' communications and on making a response which relates to the other person and best achieves the objective that one has. They also need to take account of the changing circumstances of the social landscape as an exchange of statements with another person develops. One's behaviour is socially skilled if it moves one towards achieving one's objective.

The professional helper uses counselling skills in a similar way. She identifies, say, some strong feelings or particular difficulty her client has and decides that a counselling skills 'mode' is the most appropriate way to respond. As her client begins to explain himself and to reveal his feelings so she in turn works with both of these, adjusting her communication with sensitivity to and understanding of what he says. This process of continuous adjustment to the client's statements and the consequent effect of her own contributions is monitored by the helper and set against some useful outcome or aim that she has in mind, for example that her client is helped to express his distress. What is actually seen to be desirable or possible obviously depends on her previous experience, as well as on her attitudes, beliefs and even on her philosophy of helping. It must also refer to her understanding of the process she is involved in and to an awareness of herself in this engagement.

In this book counselling skills are seen as an example of this process. Therefore we shall examine the significant elements of counselling skills and the relationships between them. In particular we focus on the importance of actually learning and being fluent in the mental and verbal skills that are the essence of a counselling attitude and counselling behaviour. However, these skills are not sufficient for the helper to understand and facilitate individual change. A counselling skills approach must also acknowledge the theoretical understanding, facilitative attitude and objective self-awareness of the helper. Figure 1 shows all of these elements and puts them into the context of helper and client. The left-hand box refers to the helper's beliefs, theories and self-awareness. These are

H E L P E R

| Beliefs, attitudes, e.g. in having respect, empathy and genuineness for the client; in wanting to help.

Theoretical understanding of the counselling process, e.g. as in client-centred counselling, or as in psychodynamic counselling.

Self-awareness, e.g. awareness of own feelings about client, or own needs in the helping relationship. | **Receiving skills:** attentive, informed selection of client's communication of self and his experience.

↓
Understanding the client (especially in *reference* to helper's beliefs, theories and her own self-awareness as described in left-hand box).

↓
Response skills: verbal and non-verbal behaviour that conveys understanding confronts client's belief's, helps him to express feelings, etc. |

←→

CLIENT

Figure 1 The elements of counselling skills behaviour

seen as directly and continuously influencing the helper's counselling skills, though they are not in themselves skills, since

9

they represent the helper's knowledge and feelings rather than her behaviour. All of these are to be discussed in later chapters. The right-hand box refers sequentially to the helper's skills of attending and listening to the client (receiving skills), of making sense of this (understanding the client) and of conveying some of this understanding back to the client (response skills). The flow of information from the client to the helper and vice versa is indicated by the arrowed lines in each direction. What remains to be identified in this chapter are these behavioural (verbal and non-verbal) skills that are referred to in the right-hand box and are seen as integral to the counsellijg skills approach.

WHAT BASIC SKILLS ARE NEEDED?

Different skills are, of course, needed for different purposes. One set of skills is useful in helping the client to tell his 'story', to express his feelings, to explain himself; additional skills may be needed for exploration and challenge of his account, to help him find greater understanding or a new perspective; different skills again may be needed to identify the means of changing things and of taking action. Quite often client change is achieved in this way. First, he unfolds and lays out his account of how things are for him so that both he and his helper can examine it closely; secondly, he understands things with more insight, begins to feel differently, perhaps to see the way ahead; thirdly, he acquires the energy for and the means of making changes in himself or in his life. Though such a sequence of events is useful to keep in mind it is not inevitable in practice and is certainly not as discretely staged as some authorities on counselling skills would have one believe. Therefore, although the following descriptions of skills are grouped around such a sequence, it does not imply that they are necesarily or even normally to be used in that order; action, especially in making minor changes, can begin early in counselling, and understanding, perhaps after a long struggle, late in the day; sometimes even there is no action, for there is nothing to be done – perhaps nothing that *can* be done.

We shall call these three groups of skills *understanding* skills, *challenging* skills and *action* skills. The actual skills to be understood, practised and eventually integrated into the helper's own persona and professional attitude to her client are listed under these three headings in Figure 2. It is these eight skills which we shall examine in more detail, discuss and illustrate in Chapter 2.

Understanding skills	Challenging skills	Action skills
Listening

Paraphrasing/ Summarising

Identifying feelings

Asking open questions | From helper's frame of reference

From client's frame of reference

From helper–client relationship | Planning action and change |

Figure 2 The basic skills of counselling

DISCUSSION ISSUES

1   What incidents have arisen in the course of your own life or work situation that you think were or would have been best met by someone using counselling skills?

2   Choose one occcasion from your own experience where you felt a counselling response was most appropriate. What skills did you or the other person present use? Which do you see as most and least helpful?

3   Which of the three definitions of counselling given in this chapter appeals to you most? Why does it appeal to you? What does your choice reveal about your own needs and understanding at this time?

4   Write down five words, each ending in '. . . ing', that in your view best represent what counselling is (omit more general words like 'helping' or 'communicating').

5   In which of the skills listed in Figure 2 do you feel you are more proficient? Which do you think are more in need of development?

2

The Basic Skills of Counselling

Having identified the basic counselling skills in the previous chapter it is now essential to say in more detail what they are and how they collectively represent a counselling sort of response. It should be said first that these skills aim primarily at enabling the client to do most of the talking, the understanding, the coming to terms with difficulties or the problem-solving; they attempt to facilitate rather than direct his thinking and feeling; they represent an empathic attitude to him – one that sensitively helps him to work with his world and the way that he, rather than the helper, sees and understands and feels about things. It may also be described as working in the client's frame of reference, in contrast to the counsellor's frame of reference. This empathic, enabling and empowering approach should pervade all of the skills, whenever and however they are used. I will have more to say about this in Chapter 3, which explains some of the theory behind counselling skills.

UNDERSTANDING SKILLS

Listening

This is the main 'receiving skill' labelled in Figure 1, though it, too, has its response behaviours as we shall see. It implies giving undivided attention to the client. Listening is the most basic and important skill. It is a specific kind of listening that is required: listening *to* and listening *for*, that is, on behalf of the other person. It is in contrast, therefore, to *conversational listening* where one attends enough to get the gist of what is said while simultaneously preparing one's own next statement. It is different, too, to *critical listening*, as in educational settings where the speaker's words are sifted for relevance and logic using an intellectual, analytical frame of reference for these purposes, and it is different from the *subjective listening* of self-interest and the more personal evaluation of what the speaker is offering you!

Attending means giving one's undivided, whole attention to somebody. This kind of listening aims first to be there for the client. It tries to follow his account moment by moment, to stay with his flow of consciousness, to try to understand what it is *like* from his point of view. At the same time such listening is not a mere recording of information; it is a search for the meaning of the client's experience; an attempt to understand how he thinks and feels about what he is actually saying. To achieve this the helper has also to leave part of herself open to notice her own reaction to what her client is communicating; to notice what his words and his expression make her think and feel almost involuntarily as she looks at him and listens to him. She is, as it were, outside of herself, observing and evaluating how she functions in relation to her client as well as simultaneously trying to recognise and intimately name what she judges to be going on in him.

I have just described something of the *internal* experience of the helper in attending and listening to her client – the receiving or perceiving skills are not necessarily reflected in the helper's observed behaviour. Notwithstanding this, she will of course make strong efforts to show her client that she is listening and giving her undivided attention in doing so. This is simply and primarily conveyed by her non-verbal behaviour.

It is easy to become too prescriptive or overly dogmatic about the helper's non-verbal communication of attention in her counselling. There is no single best way of doing it. Variations can and do occur because of the physical environment in which counselling skills are used (see pp. 75–6), because of the helper's personal style of attending, for example physically static or changing posture, because of the kind of relationship which exists between helper and client, or because of the ongoing dynamic at any particular time of the counselling; for example the helper may lean forward or move closer when her client is distressed.

Nevertheless it is important to communicate attention by giving continuous eye-contact (by which I mean to look at the client's eyes or face) *when the client is speaking*. In our culture this is normal practice, unless it is impracticable for other reasons, for example use of telephone, or because one or both parties are occupied in a way that hinders eye-contact. If one does not give eye-contact while the other is speaking this is a powerful disincentive to the speaker and he may hesitate, stutter, become less sure of what he is saying or even be stopped in mid-speech! On the other hand the speaker does not usually give continuous eye-contact to the listener. Typically, people signal their intentions to begin or end their speaking by making eye-contact and glancing back intermittently to monitor the other's response. Continuous eye-contact *made by the speaker* gives intensity or heavy emphasis (as in a telling-off!) to what is being said. Thus, the helper would not normally expect to *receive* much eye-contact whilst her client speaks, although she herself continues to scan the speaker's eyes and face attentively. This attention is maintained on her part even through silences, because the helper wishes to communicate to her client that she is still 'with him', sensitive to his being with her and ready for what he may want to say next.

Other factors in non-verbally communicating attention are the helper's posture, orientation to her client and importantly, her own facial expression. Again, much has been written about position of chairs (face to face or at 45° to each other), sitting upright, relaxed and so on, but although these factors may affect attention-giving, they may themselves be more radically affected by the circumstances of the meeting. The client may be in bed, in a wheelchair, or in his own living-room full of heavy furniture; he may be standing because there are no seats around; he may be exercising or receiving treatment because that is the context of meeting the helper; he may be in a car, driving with his manager to meet business contacts. Most of these immediately preclude fine adjustment to the counselling environment. However, if an effort is made by the helper to converse on the same physical level as her client, for example not to *stand* at a client's bedside or next to his wheelchair and if she facially communicates calm and concern together with fairly constant eye-contact, then the client becomes aware of the inner effort the helper is making to understand him.

It is also true that giving undivided attention and listening actively for meaning and feeling requires concentration, effort and even mental stamina. When the client brings something to the counselling which reminds the counsellor of events in her own life this may provoke a loss of concentration and a failure to hear or understand what is said. This is not necessarily disastrous and the ground is usually made up or retrieved in some way. If, however, the client's concern's constantly trigger the counsellor into more powerful thoughts and feelings about her own life then there may not be much point in going on with the session, and she may feel obliged to say as much to her client. This then becomes a supervision issue, something we will give space to in Chapter 6.

Listening itself is a silent activity. It is difficult, using only the written word, to convey the power of listening or to provide a telling example. But Carl Rogers (1980: 42) quotes Lâo-tse, the Chinese sage who lived around 500BC, and who beautifully captures the self-insight from and therapeutic value of being emphatically listened to:

> It is as though he listened
> and such listening as his enfolds us in silence
> in which at last we begin to hear
> what we are meant to be.

Paraphrasing

Paraphrasing is a response skill (Figure 1), as are most of the other basic skills discussed in this chapter. Paraphrasing means expressing or restating what the client has said in other words – in this case the helper's own words. In practice, paraphrasing may use words similar to those the client has used, or, at the other extreme, completely different words. There is no merit in changing words for the sake of change. The intention is to capture and accurately express the meaning of what the client says. More than that, perhaps, to say what the client wanted to say or was trying to say if, in his difficulty, he is unable to find the right words.

Another description of this kind of helper response is

15

'reflecting'. It is a term originally used by Carl Rogers (1980: 138–9, for example) who described an empathic response partly as 'reflecting feelings'. He also describes how the popular use of the word 'reflecting' degenerated to the point where it meant merely repeating back the last few words the client had said, so that Rogers himself stopped using the term altogether for some time. Richard Nelson-Jones (1983: 49) refers to 'reflection of content' and 'reflection of feeling', implying in the former a helper response similar to paraphrasing. He is careful to point out the difference between the reflection of content and the mere parroting back of the client's words. He illustrates the absurdity of slavish repetition with a story about a counsellor working with a suicidal client in an office near the top of a tall building:

Client: I feel terrible.
Counsellor: You feel terrible.
Client: I feel really terrible.
Counsellor: You feel really terrible.
Client: For two cents I would jump out of that window there.
Counsellor: For two cents you would jump out of that window there.
Client: Here I go.
Counsellor: There you go.
Client: (*lands on the pavement below with a thud*)
Counsellor: Thud!

Merely repeating the client's words back to him has severe limitations. It may, as I have said, simply fail to grasp the client's intended meaning, or it may feel artificial to the helper, betraying her own effort to be authentic in the counselling situation. It may be perceived by the client as odd, especially if it is carried out deliberately or somewhat mechanically as might happen in the early stages of learning counselling skills.

It is important, therefore, for the learner to appreciate the quite basic purposes of a behaviour like paraphrasing which draws attention to the experience and thinking of the client rather than that of the helper. It is a step in the development of a dialogue between helper and client, the aim of which is to reveal the client's unique experience and to assist him to become clearer about what is happening and what he wants to happen in his world. The helper is saying: 'This is what I think you are telling me' and her statement, in turn, is there to be heard and responded to.

Another significant purpose of paraphrasing is to communicate understanding. It is clear from her paraphrasing that the helper has received and made sense of the client's words. The client realises from the helper's response that he has been understood. Better still, the helper seems to know what the client's experience is like *to him* rather than how it is merely represented in words. Accurate and sensitive paraphrasing seems somehow to transcend the medium, the employment of verbal skills, as empathy for the client is developed. Thus, the client begins to think of the helper as an understanding person. He attributes to the helper this quality of empathy, or the ability to understand others as they see themselves and their own life situations – one of the essential conditions for an effective counselling relationship that we will examine in Chapter 3.

Paraphrasing, therefore, is almost the life-blood of the counselling interaction. It establishes the client's meanings, carries them forward and provides the opportunity for stimulating further response and greater understanding. In the hands of skilled helpers or counsellors it is a powerful tool to gain access to the client's experience so that it is available to both parties in their joint task of understanding, gaining insight and beginning to recognise the possibility of change.

How does this work in practice? Here is an example of how paraphrasing might be used in a conversation between Angela, who is a residential care worker and one of her residents, Fred, who is unhappy about the way he seems always to be landed with other residents' domestic chores:

Angela: You're looking a bit down in the mouth, Fred, what's happening?

Fred: It's George – he should be laying the table but he's left me to do it again.

Angela: So George has left it to you, has he?

Fred: Yeah, and it's not the first time either – I'm fed up with it.

Angela: It's getting you down because it keeps happening.

Fred: He knows if he leaves it long enough someone

else will do it – usually me.

Angela: He's taking advantage of you, then, it feels like he is manipulating you, almost.

Fred: That's right – he knows I'm a soft touch.

In this exchange Angela has not introduced anything from her own view of the situation. She may already have her suspicions about George's attitude to sharing the work, and she may wonder to what extent Fred actually invites others to put things on to him so that he gets a pay-off in being able to complain about them, at the same time casting himself in the role of long-suffering toiler in the cause of right and justice. All this may be true but at the moment she is trying to get Fred to tell the story the way he himself sees it. Importantly, by staying with what Fred was saying she has allowed him 'space' or opportunity enough to mention his own vulnerability at the end of this piece of the conversation. Notice, too, that Fred picks up Angela's slightly elaborated statement about his being manipulated and actually affirms this with 'That's right'. Angela is probably in a better position to probe Fred's own attitude to things than she was at the beginning of the conversation.

Summarising

Summarising is much like a longer version of paraphrasing. It is a spoken précis or a résumé of the content of the counselling or of what the client has been saying, especially, as sometimes happens, if he has been talking, uninterrupted, for several minutes or more. Summarising, though, has several important uses which are different from those of paraphrasing:

1 It provides an opportunity for the helper to check out that she is getting hold of the important elements of the client's account. Occasionally, and typically at the beginning of a first counselling session a client may pour out his troubles in a garbled or incoherent way. Some things are apparently unrelated to others, in the helper's perception, or so much has been said that she perhaps feels confused by the sheer volume of it all. It may be appropriate in these instances even to interrupt the client to put a 'helper's-eye-view' of what has taken place back into the proceedings. The helper

may begin by saying something like: 'Let me see if I have understood you properly. You're telling me that you . . .' or, 'I'm not sure I've got all this right, but you are saying you . . .'.

2   Summarising is also a useful way to begin or end a session. If the helper can establish what has been more significant in the time spent with the client and point to this in a few sentences, this is useful for the client to refer to – either after the counselling when he thinks over what was said and how he felt about it, or during the summary when this itself provides a review and perhaps a new point of focus. It is also an opportunity for the helper to confirm tasks or action that have been agreed during the session.

It is sometimes a help to start the session by referring back to the content of the previous one even though the helper does not set out to refer to everything that transpired on the previous occasion. For example: 'I remember last time we talked a lot about people taking advantage of you. Is that still important or are there other things on your mind right now?'

3   Summarising is helpful, too, in offering to clients a review of the work that has been done thus far and subsequently inviting them to identify what matters most to them, or, in other words, to establish a focus for the counselling ahead. Thus a helper (perhaps Angela to Fred in the residential home) might say: 'You have explained how difficult it is for you when George doesn't bother about the jobs that have to be done, and that you feel you are easily taken advantage of. Then again you think the staff could do more to help with supervision of jobs. Which of these should we talk about first?'

Summarising, then, can address the content or the process of counselling, the latter especially in reviewing the session just ended and the way in which it helped or failed to do so. In this a summary may also refer to the client's feelings about what has transpired. So far, little has been said about feelings and how the helper understands and responds to these and it is this we consider next.

Identifying feelings

Paraphrasing, by definition, refers to what the client has actually said. In the event he may have stated explicitly what his feelings were (as Fred said he was 'fed up'), or, as is very often the case, merely implied them (as Eric, whose wife was bed-ridden and very weak, might have said: 'The fact that she is where she is means the end is in sight – and that's something I don't want to think about' – implying, maybe, his apprehension, fear, his own vulnerability or self-doubt, even panic).

Because counselling has much to do with the recognition and expression of feelings, the helper must be sensitive to this inner flow of emotion and appropriately help her client to describe his feelings and to recognise their meaning for him. In practice, this is not always easy to achieve. Our culture does not favour openness about feelings. Men especially are discouraged from expressing or even speaking of their anxiety or distress. Some families repress negative feelings so that members do not show anger or hurt, for example. The eventual result may be that feelings are not consciously experienced, much less recognised or expressed. So at one extreme the helper may have to respond to feelings that are openly and uninhibitedly released (for example the grief of bereavement among those who grow up in an Afro-Caribbean culture) and, at the other, to have to guess at what is going on in her client when he smiles as he describes what sounds like a very painful experience for him!

However, the helper uses her own experience, her imagination, her intelligence, sensitivity and a developing ability to understand and 'tune in' to what her client is feeling in order to recognise and to identify his particular emotions in words that best describe them. Not that there is any shortage of these, either. Roget's Thesaurus has some forty-five pages, or about 17,000 words on feelings, listed in three sections: Affections generally; Personal (affections); and Sympathetic (affections). Of course there is much repetition in this, but there is also the reminder of how limited our vocabulary can be in trying to circumscribe an emotion. Here, for example, are some of the words following the 'nervousness' section of *Fear*: want of courage, lack of confidence, cowardliness, cowardice, self-distrust, shyness, modesty, timidity, fearfulness, hesitation, avoidance, loss of nerve, cold feet, fears, misgiving, apprehensiveness, worry, defeatism, hopelessness, trepidation. Which of these, if any, might have been the right words to describe what Eric was feeling as he began to realise that his wife may not live much longer?

The most commonly recognisable, that is, observed, emotions are *anger, depression, anxiety, joy, surprise, fear* and *disgust*. One may think of each of these as existing across a wide range of intensities from mild to strong. For example, fear might vary in degree from terror, through fright and fearfulness to unease.

In practice, identifying feelings is not separated from paraphrasing content. It is separated here in order to give emphasis to the whole idea of the helper's awareness of and responsiveness to the client's emotions in the course of counselling. In the process of doing this the helper is also teaching the client to notice what is going on inside himself and thus to build a climate in which both parties are mutually sensitive to the changing flow of feelings in the client and to the benefits that follow from understanding one's feelings and being able to live with them in constructive and health-giving ways.

Let us go back to the conversation between Angela and Fred, who are now sitting down in an adjacent, more private room:

Angela: You said you'd had enough of George, because he knows you're a soft touch.

Fred: He makes me sick – you'd think this place existed just for him, the way he acts.

Angela: You really loathe his selfish attitude.

Fred: Yes but at the same time I despise myself for giving in every time – it just seems that everybody else has to pay for the way he is.

Angela: Mmmm! ... it's not fair and you hate going through with it.

Fred: Well, there you are, but is it worth all the hassle if I tell him what I think?

Angela: It seems as though you're not sure if you want to do anything about it, even now.

Fred: Well I would if I had some support.

Here, Angela has helped Fred to become clearer about his own feelings and how, now, they might be used to achieve a more satisfactory oucome for him. She sticks pretty well to what Fred actually says and probably Fred begins to see her as a supporter and, perhaps, as a means of solving his problem. Perhaps Angela could help him to clarify his last statement by using the fourth of the understanding skills, that is, by asking an open question: 'What kind of support are you hoping for?'

Asking open questions

The business of asking questions in the pursuit of understanding our client and his experience raises, in turn, its own questions: why do we need to ask questions? Whose understanding of the client's situation is more important? What kind of questions, if we are to use them at all, are helpful?

Beginners in the field of counselling skills sometimes imagine that it is necessary to ask a lot of questions in order to get a proper picture of what is going on. On the contrary, the client who is intensely and often painfully aware of his difficulties usually needs few questions in order to articulate them. Further, it is yet again vitally important that the helper listen very carefully to what he actually says, *how* he says it and *what he leaves out* or somehow fails to speak about. Questions are used mainly to enable him to develop his statements, to refer to his feelings or to detail or clarify what the counselling senses is an important issue for her client. In saying that, it should still be noticed that questions are generally a subsidiary way of getting the client to tell his story, since the skills of paraphrasing and identifying feelings are potent ways of promoting the client's account of himself and have the virtue of not directing the client's attention to what is sometimes the wrong issue or emphasis.

The obvious danger is that questions are more helper-centred than client-centred; that they arise primarily out of the helper's experience and refer to her well-established and professional ways of constructing, diagnosing and solving problems; in situations that demand a counselling response this will be inappropriate and unhelpful. Questions that seem to follow one line or a specific purpose tend to pervert the client's own view of what is happening as they refer more and more to the authority of the helper and her need to control the conversation.

I referred at the beginning of this section to 'open' questions in the belief that these kinds of questions are generally preferable to certain other, more controlling types of questions which are described below. Examples of each type of question are followed by a comparable version of a preferred open question. All the questions might have been part of the continued conversation between Angela and Fred in their residential care setting.

Closed question ('closed', because this type of question limits the answer to 'yes', 'no' or requires some other specific piece of information): 'Are you going to confront George or not?'

Preferred open question: 'How do you feel you will be able to deal with George, now?'

Leading question ('leading', because some value, preference or bias is built into the question, partly specifying the answer; the classic example is: 'Have you stopped beating your wife?'): 'How long are you going to let this thing drag on for?'

Preferred open question: 'How are you going to cope with this in the future?'

'Why?' question ('why?' questions are often not facilitative because they may induce intellectual or deductive explanations of a client's experience. Worse, they may cast the helper in the role of expert gatherer of information, analyser and thus, by implication, finder of solutions; this creates false expectations in the client and prevents him from doing more insightful work himself): 'Why are you always complaining?' or 'Why do you think you're a soft touch?'

Preferred open questions: 'How do you feel about this?' or 'Could you tell me some more about that?' or 'What do you mean when you say you're a soft touch?'

These four basic skills, listening, paraphrasing/summarising, identifying feelings and asking open questions, have the prime purpose of enabling the client to tell about himself; to explain and to examine what is going on in his life. They are also an important way of communicating the helper's non-directive

23

attitude to her client and of establishing a relationship in which the client feels safe and supported enough to begin to explore in more depth his own beliefs, attitudes and feelings, which are implicated in his present difficulties. The helper's contribution to this is in the next block of skills which challenge the client to seek a new awareness of himself.

CHALLENGING SKILLS

Counselling is about change. If it is to achieve the purposes presented in Chapter 1, i.e., 'to come to terms with a new experience', 'realise assets', 'reduce anxiety', 'face the problem more objectively', 'decide what to do about it' and so on, then these all imply change for the client. He achieves this by becoming more aware of himself and perhaps of others, too; more generally by understanding how he is affected by his social and physical environment – by work and home, for example; and especially by establishing a new perspective or a new understanding of himself and his situation.

This latter type of change is sometimes called 'reframing', implying that if the client chooses a different 'window' or point of view as he metaphorically travels around and through the problem then he begins to understand it differently. The relationships, the construction of elements are not as he first saw them. They may begin to appear less rigid, more accessible to change; ways and means of doing this may become more obvious.

Some of this 'reframing' can begin to take place as the client tells his story. To explain oneself at length and in detail to an attentive other person is a primary means of reviewing a difficulty. The burden is unloaded, placed between helper and client and can be inspected and appraised by both. Helpers who 'only' listen attentively are important agents for unburdening the pain and starting the process of change. Nevertheless the interventions we now describe as 'challenging skills' are more conspicuously and intentionally made to enable the client to achieve these changes.

Challenging skills promote the opportunity for change and enable the client to use this opportunity as best he can. They are aimed at raising his awareness by using one of the following three sources of challenge:

From the helper's frame of reference: i.e., from her perspective; from her observation of her client; from understanding of her client's situation and her knowledge of situations like this. Where the helper has special skills or knowledge connected with, say, health or social care, these are sometimes used within the counselling session.

From the client's frame of reference: i.e., from the periphery of his perspective on his difficulty; constructions which are implied but not spoken; feelings that are unrecognised or unexpressed; emerging themes; and so on. All of these are responded to by the use of the helper's *deeper empathy*. She helps her client to become more fully aware when he appears to have only an inkling of what is going on.

From the helper–client relationship: from the helper's deliberate and explicit reference to the ongoing relationship between herself and her client.

These skills, therefore, imply a move away from the client-centredness that characterises the understanding skills. They do so in an attempt to introduce material that is at present just outside but still within reach of the client's awareness and understanding.

In using challenging skills the old song applies: 'It's not (just) what you do – it's the way that you do it.' Sue Culley (1991: 71) in her detailed and very practical book, *Integrative Counselling Skills*, suggests that in general a challenge needs to be:

1   Tentative, for example, 'I'm wondering if you ...' or 'How does this seem to you?'
2   Related to the contract, to the shared understanding of why you are talking about this to the client; in other words it needs to be within the present context and relevant to what is being said at the time.
3   Sensitive to the client's readiness, not too early in the development of the helper–client relationship, checking that the client is not too distressed or defensive, and is therefore able to receive and use the challenge.
4   Close to the client's experience, dealing with something that has probably already been touched on in some aspect

and is expressed in such a way that the client can understand and see the implications for himself.
5 Concrete, not general or vague, specific about behaviour,
thoughts, statements or feelings.

With this advice in mind we will now look at the three kinds
of challenge listed above.

Challenges from the helper's frame of reference

These challenges are themselves divisible into further categories: giving factual information; giving personal information;
picking up themes and inconsistencies.

Giving factual information

Either the client asks for information or the helper judges it
helpful to give it. It does not follow that just because it is
asked for, the best way forward is to give it, or that if it is seen
as helpful in principle it should necessarily be offered in the
same terms as asked for. All of which may seem evasive on
the helper's part but we are reminded once again of the importance of making the helper's response or challenge accessible
to the client.

A client may sometimes ask for the helper's view on his
situation or himself or what he should do next. If this is related
to the counselling aspects of his situation it may be more
important to explore why he wants the helper's opinion than
to give the information itself. For example, a distressed client
may say: 'I sometimes think I'm going mad – what do you
think?' The helper may say something like: 'It sounds like
my opinion is important to you' (identifying feelings) perhaps
adding: 'I wonder how it would help if I told you', or she may
decide it is more appropriate to say: 'I've found you very upset
and a bit disjointed at times – but I don't think that's going
mad.'

Information-giving may also be connected with the helper's
primary professional role, for example as a nurse, line manager, teacher or social worker, when the client may benefit
from knowing more about treatment, union activities, house
procedures or the existence of other helping agencies. For

example, staff nurse Betty talks to Carol about the major surgery she has just had:

> *Carol:* Now I've had the operation I feel low and sort of without any belief in myself.
>
> *Betty:* It seems to have knocked all the go out of you. (*understanding paraphrase*) I'm wondering if you've heard of the support group that was set up to help those who have had your operation? (*challenge – giving information*)

Alternatively, Betty might have given information that arose from her experience of the job. She could have said: 'It will take some time to get used to it. Many people feel much more positive after a week or so.' Neither of these statements is especially empathic and they are in general the kind of thing that counsellors as such tend to avoid. Furthermore it is possible, because we know nothing of what has already been said, that Betty is wide of the mark in one or both cases. On the other hand, if Betty is using her counselling skills well, this may be exactly the information that Carol has need of.

Giving personal information

Using the helper's own similar or related life experience is usually called 'self-disclosure'. The pros and cons of self-disclosure are considered in detail in Nelson-Jones (1983: 163–9). He proposes its use in encouraging clients who find it difficult to start talking about themselves, to communicate counsellor genuineness and to offer the client the counsellor's experience as a relevant example from which he may be able to profit. Against this is the danger that the client may see a statement about the helper's own life as irrelevant, intrusive and unempathic. In practice, inappropriate self-disclosure on the helper's side often results in the client's continuing with his own statement without reference to what the helper has said.

It was possible for Betty to have given Carol some personal information in response to Carol's statement 'Now I've had the operation I feel low and sort of without any belief in myself', such as: 'I had an operation myself two years ago and I felt very apprehensive and groggy for several days afterwards.' Betty's reply, as given here, is a clear example of

27

self-disclosure. However, there are no clues about the context of the two statements and it is impossible to judge whether or not Betty's reply would help Carol to benefit, say, by revising her own expectations of how she should feel. It may be useful for the reader to imagine some of the conditions or an extension of the conversation within which Betty's replay would be seen as more certainly helpful.

Picking up themes and inconsistencies

The helper sometimes notices inconsistences in what her client is saying. The client is not aware of them and they are not necessarily a source of discomfort or dissonance, but when the helper picks up things that don't fit well or make good sense to her, then it could be important for her client to attend to these things so that his own approach becomes more consistent and integrated. Once again we stress the word 'could'. Because a contradiction is noticed, it is not inevitable that verbally identifying it will help. Clients' defences are not there to be attacked or somehow exploded; rather to be taken down brick-by-brick as a joint enterprise and keeping the conditions in mind that we have already talked about on pages 25–6.

On other occasions, though, it can be very useful to challenge a client's inconsistent thinking: here, once again, is Betty, this time trying to help Carol be a little more realistic about leaving hospital to return home:

> *Carol:* Of course Bob wants what's best for me but I wouldn't expect him to take time off work to help me at home.
>
> *Betty:* I'm wondering if there isn't a contradiction in that, Carol. On the one hand you are telling me that Bob wants what is best for you but on the other you say you don't want him to make a special effort when it really matters.

A similar kind of challenge can arise from the helper's observation that her clients seem to repeat things dogmatically or frequently return to a particular topic or way of seeing things. She notices that this somehow restricts her clients' understanding, causing them to behave rather without due regard to what is actually going on around them. Thus, we may find Betty saying to Carol:

> *Betty:* You were saying yesterday that you weren't expecting Bob to take any time off work, nor do you want to delay having the girls back home; also your mother would like to be more involved but you won't let her . . . it's beginning to make me think that you have something to prove – am I right?

Carol's theme seems to be about showing her independence. Other themes may reflect 'shoulds' and 'oughts', usually learned very early in life, such as not to be worth much, not to take risks, not to show feeling, not to be yourself and so on. Themes may also imply constant striving; Transactional Analysis (another approach to counselling) identifies the Five Drivers: Be Perfect; Be Strong; Try Hard; Please Others; Hurry Up (see for example Stewart and Joines 1987: 131).

Finally, we must note that the source of all these challenges, the helper's frame of reference; that is, *her* reasoning, *her* experience, *her* know-how or know-about, is immediately outside and may even be some way off from the client's present experiencing – there is a risk not only of it not being helpful, but also of it being unhelpful and setting the counselling back a bit. In this respect challenging out of the helper's experience may immediately cast her back, in the client's view, into her more usual authoritative helper role and work against her efforts to be facilitative and to promote her client's own authority and control. For example, when Betty gave Carol an 'answer' (join the support group) this might also have been taken as a signal to end the conversation. The question of a helper implicitly or explicitly taking on the role of counsellor is one we will return to later.

Challenges from the client's frame of reference

In one sense it appears contradictory to talk of extending the client's awareness from *within* his own frame of reference. However, as I suggested at the beginning of the section on challenging skills, what is brought to his awareness are the things which seem to be on the periphery, implied but not spoken, in the air but not identified. They are things which, as the helper experiences it, are coming from her client, yet somehow he does not own or acknowledge them.

The ability to pick up these unspoken or vaguely expressed messages is sometimes called 'deeper empathy'. Before we examine the concept of deeper empathy, though, it is sensible to consider what the term empathy itself refers to.

Empathy is an important concept in counselling. Rather than a skill or a piece of observable behaviour empathy describes an underlying attitude or approach to the client which employs the understanding skills of listening, para-phrasing and summarising, identifying feelings and asking open questions. It has been extensively and illuminatingly written of by Carl Rogers. Empathy is entering what Rogers (1980: 142) called 'the private perceptual world of the other' and 'being sensitive moment by moment to the changing felt meanings which flow in the other person . . . appreciating the way he sees things and what his experience means to him'. Empathy is one of what are generally called the 'core con-ditions' or essential characteristics of the effective counselling relationship and we will meet it again in connection with counselling theory in the next chapter.

Deeper empathy (or 'advanced empathy' as for example, Egan (1975: 127) has called it) shares the same essential atti-tude to the client but refers to the material that he implicitly rather than explicitly communicates; to thoughts and feelings that are half-glimpsed or hinted at; experiences that are hazy, obscured or appear to be unnoticed. Rogers (1980: 144) talks of deeper empathy as beginning to uncover and voice 'feeling areas and meanings of which the client is scarcely aware'. In using deeper empathy the helper's skills lie first in sensing these underlying aspects of the client's experience and second in communicating some of these sensings back to him with care and understanding. The helper's challenges in deeper empathy, therefore, arise from her appreciation of where the client *is* in his experiencing, and if she is accurate in this her challenges will still be within his reach, to be grasped, recognised and accommodated as understandings that he can now consciously use to change and move forward.

Here is Carol, in the surgical ward talking again to her staff nurse, Betty:

Carol: Bob's bringing the children with him this evening.
Betty: You'll be pleased to see them, I expect.
Carol: Well, I like to see them all ... but it's difficult to cope with them all at once and there's nothing I can do to help; in a way, I'd rather see them at home.
Betty: You can't be a proper mum to them in here, is that what you are feeling?
Carol: (starts to cry) I feel I'm letting them down by being ill and not being around ...
Betty: (waits) Maybe you are beginning to wonder how it's going to be in the future – it's all rather uncertain isn't it?
Carol: Yes, that's the worst bit.

Betty has helped Carol to face some of her deepest fears about herself, her illness and the uncertain future. This is difficult and painful, but by doing so she will be both more realistic and more positive about her rehabilitation and subsequent life at home with her family. It is easy for helpers, especially less experienced ones, to shy away from the deeper and sometimes more painful issues. Most of us do not find it easy to stay with pain or distress in others; sometimes it is easier to collude with the client in acting as though it isn't important or it's better somehow to cover it up or smooth it over. The helper who can both sense the underlying anxiety and/or sorrow, and carefully bring it to the light to be examined and faced for what it is, is performing a skilled and valuable service for her client who may be confused, frightened and psychologically disabled by what is happening to him. This is one use of deeper empathy and it illustrates the importance of staying close to the client's experience and his way of understanding this.

Challenges from the helper–client relationship

The third and final source of challenges to the client are those that are drawn from the ongoing relationship or person-to-person interaction between the helper and her client. This itself may be seen to have three aspects:

1   The 'what is going on between us?' aspect of the counselling relationship. This is sometimes called 'immediacy' and

refers to the 'here-and-now' of the interaction between helper and client, as, for example, in 'We have been talking about this for ten minutes or more, yet I don't feel we are dealing with what matters!' This is essentially how either or both parties see the relationship, the dynamics of their working together.

2 How the client personifies or relates to the helper, especially because he brings with him ways of understanding or feeling for other people that are formed from his previous and in particular his early experience in life. This is usually called client transference.

3 How the helper personifies or reacts to the client is reciprocal fashion to (2) (helper's transference), but also the effect of her being partly drawn into this by the client's transference (this is called the helper's countertransference).

Immediacy

This is the skill of observing the changing relationship with the client and of engaging the client himself both in the discussion and the management of this where it is relevant to the client's concerns. For example Betty might say to Carol: 'We talked about some very personal and upsetting things today – how do you feel now about the discussion we've had – I mean how would you like to go on from here?'; or, perhaps earlier in the counselling relationship, Betty may have decided it would be useful to clarify a possible joint purpose by saying to Carol: 'I've come to see if you would like to spend some time talking about how you feel now you have had the operation' or (later) 'I feel as though we have rather rushed through things today – perhaps that's because I'm short of time – what do you think?'

Client transference

The transference is the expectations and beliefs that the client has about the helper. They are not consciously owned and, as I have said, often date back to early childhood and to the client's own parenting. For example, although Betty, in her counselling, tries to work in a non-authoritative way, Carol may nevertheless adopt an attitude of over-dependence or deference towards Betty because she expects nurses in general to take decisions on a patient's behalf and not to spend much time discussing their patients' feelings about what is happening in hospital. Thus, Carol's attitude to nurses in general transfers to this particular nurse, Betty, and affects the way she sees Betty and behaves towards her.

Transference can be about sexuality or gender, for example when a client says to the helper of the opposite sex: 'You're a woman (or man) – you wouldn't understand!' Such a statement refers to the client's previous experience of women (or men) adopted from his or her own parents. Another common transference experienced by professional helpers is the client's unrealistically positive feelings for them (positive transference). They may feel themselves loved, revered, identified with, idolised and so on, to the extent that the helping relationship becomes unbalanced and does not address the client's original difficulties. Instead, the helper may now choose to identify the transference with her client and use it for the client's benefit.

Thus the helper challenges her client to look at his own need for an authority figure, for a perfect leader or an object of love, to try to understand this and to be aware of the ways in which it affects his interaction with particular others, for example his managers at work, his own parents and in this instance, his professional helper. What commonly happens in transferences like these is that the helper sooner or later 'fails' her client in being unable to meet his expectations and this too becomes part of the helper's challenge to the client. For example Carol might say to Betty: 'You must have seen a lot of patients like me – tell me how to deal with my worries' or 'We have spent a lot of time talking about my fears, but you haven't come up with any answers yet'. Betty's response to these transference statements must be sensitive to Carol's own position. There may be enough challenge in letting Carol hear again what she has said: 'You want me to tell you how to deal with your worries' or a little more pointedly 'You expect someone like *me* to tell you how to deal with your worries, but is that realistic?'

Similarly, in response to the earlier client statement about the opposite sex not understanding, a helper might say: 'You feel that women (men) wouldn't understand this'; or, more strongly: 'You say that women wouldn't understand this – could we talk some more about that?'

Helper transference

The helper transference arises in the same way as the client transference. However, both its availability for and its usefulness in challenging a client are in doubt because this is material that in the first place is unconscious and in the second is probably unconnected with the client's immediate concerns. However, it may be that Betty's dawning awareness of herself as admiring Carol's determination and courage in facing up to her difficulties is something she clarifies in discussion with her supervisor and deliberately chooses to share with Carol at a time when Carol can use this. The reader may like to consider the disadvantages of sharing helper transferences, even those that are very much 'for' the client, as this one is.

The countertransference is more potent. Here the helper is unconsciously pushed or manipulated into a complementary attitude by her client; again, 'child' to 'parent' is common, but notice, too, the countertransference that could arise from: 'You're a woman – you wouldn't understand' in the form of a personal defence such as 'I may be a woman, but I have a lot of experience of working with men and I do know what you're talking about'. As a blind or unaware response, this is probably of little value. On the other hand, sensitively and appropriately used it may help the client to take a new look at his helper.

ACTION SKILLS

The skills we discuss finally – planning action and change – are usually there in some form at the beginning of counselling. What does the client want to happen? What changes is he looking for? How could the situation he is in be improved? These initial questions may be unclear, unrealistic or premature, but they are around, simply because at the moment life is uncomfortable and something has to be done about it. Talking to someone who has counselling skills is a positive first step. As the understanding develops so the questions about change are clarified or reformed. Sooner or later, perhaps when some of the ground has been consolidated, or a new perspective emerges, the question of what action to take is more obviously in focus. The important point about this process, though, is that action, if action is required, arises from insight and understanding – from the struggle to see oneself and one's situation more clearly. In other words change (in this case internal change) precedes action just as that action will in turn promote further change. Each depends upon the other.

The helper's skills in promoting action and change must take several considerations into account. First, as with the challenging skills they must relate to what the client is seeking, where he is 'at' and whether he is ready to tackle this. Secondly, they must somehow avoid confusion with her prescriptive or authoritative role which, perhaps, has already provided appropriate injunction and advice to the client on other aspects of his work, social or health careers. They must be facilitative, not prescriptive, even though the client may be expecting the latter rather than the former. In this respect it is useful to know how to respond when clients actually ask for advice about action when the helper feels it inappropriate or ultimately unhelpful to give this. For example, in response to a client asking: 'What would you do in my situation?', the helper may simply say that she believes it is not helpful to give advice, rather she would prefer they explored possible actions together. Nor is it too disingenuous to say: 'You would like to know what I would do, but I believe that what I would do is

---

What do you think you could do about this?

What would you like to do about this?

Can you think of a realistic way forward?

What do you want to see happen next?

How do you feel you could achieve this?

How could this be dealt with?

What do you feel would help?

How could other people help?

How do you see this working out?

How do you see things changing?

Figure 3   Questions to help a client look ahead and plan action

not necessarily the best thing for you – and that's what we are here to work on.' To enable the client to focus on action and change, to begin to consider possibilities, plans and ways of moving forward, questions like those in Figure 3 may be used.

When taking action or making more obvious changes is clearly the main part of the counselling business, then a more direct approach is employed. For example, where clients want to change some aspect of their lifestyle, perhaps to control eating or use of alcohol, or where clients wish to change their behaviour within a relationship, or to be more assertive at work, then it may be appropriate to concentrate on these goals and how to achieve them. Some of the above imply more extensive forms of education or training such as is offered by Well-Women Clinics, the Health Education Authority's 'Look After Your Heart/Look After Yourself' project or assertiveness groups. Others may be tackled by using a stress management or problem-solving approach like that offered by Gerard Egan under the title of Force-Field Analysis (Egan 1975: 200). The following are the essential steps in the process:

1 Write a sentence or so that describe the (undesirable) situation you are in.
2 Write another sentence describing the situation *as you would like it to be* (i.e., identify the changes you want to achieve and believe are possible).
3 On one side of the paper list the forces that prevent you from or hinder you in making this change. On the other side list the forces that help you in making this change, as in Figure 4, for example.
4 Choose one of the hindering forces that may be amenable to change and brainstorm some action steps that would reduce or eliminate that force. For example, action steps to reduce the hindering force 'I am afraid of George' could be: 'Try talking to George at mealtimes. Tell myself there's nothing to be afraid of. Remind myself that I have Angela's support.'
5 Choose a helping force that seems to be important in promoting change and brainstorm action steps that would bring this into play. For example, action steps to promote the helping force 'Angela's support' could be: 'Arrange regular meetings with Angela and *be there!* Tackle George

Name: Fred Rollinson.
Situation as it is now: George makes my life difficult and unpleasant.
Situation as I would like it to be: George treats me with respect.

Helping forces	*Hindering forces*
a Angela's support.	a I am afraid of George.
b I *want* to change.	b George makes me look
c Other people dislike	stupid.
George's attitude.	c I don't know how to
d Angela says	deal with it without
assertiveness training	ending in a row.
might help.	d Other people might be
	against me.

Figure 4 Helping and hindering forces in making changes

while Angela is around. Get Angela to help me practise.'
6   Select the action steps that are most practicable, in line with your own values.
7   Review, re-evaluate the situation, repeat steps 4–6 as now seems appropriate.

DISCUSSION ISSUES

1   We can only understand others through experience of ourselves, both in the past and, in the counselling mode, in the present. Therefore empathy, as Carl Rogers describes it, is a non-starter – or is it?
2   Recall the effective listening style of three people that you know well. From these examples identify some of the elements of good listening.
3   Write down five or six words that describe degrees of feeling ranging from 'mild' to 'intense' for each of the following: anxiety; depression; surprise. Consider the usefulness of these words in relation to particular clients that you know of.
4   Can you begin, maintain and end a casual conversation with someone else staying the whole time with their concerns (say for about 3–5 minutes)?

5 Now that you have read this chapter, again assess yourself on the basic skills of counselling. Tick the box that most nearly coincides with your self-evaluation.

Understanding skills	Weak	Adequate	Very good
Listening			
Paraphrasing/ summarising			
Identifying feelings			
Asking open questions			

Challenging skills			
From helper's frame of reference			
From client's frame of reference			
From helper–client relationship			

Action skills			
Planning action and change			

3

Theory and Practice

WHAT IS THEORY?

As Figure 1 illustrates (p. 9), theory is an integral part of the counselling skills function. We cannot operate without it, even though sometimes we may think we are doing so. Theory acts as a reference body; as a set of guidelines on how to proceed if we want to progress in a given way or towards a particular goal. It determines our attitude to the work and to our clients; it governs our approach and our continuing awareness of the counselling skills process. It enables us to interpret what is happening in the counselling, to reflect on these happenings and even to evaluate them against our intentions or our understanding of how things ought to happen in the best interests of our clients. Therefore it offers a kind of intellectual management of the counselling process. In short, theory is an indispensable partner to counselling practice.

What exactly *is* theory, then? How does it come to exist? In essence it is a kind of received wisdom. In the first place it usually represents one person's way of thinking about the counselling process. Whether that person is called Sigmund Freud or Carl Rogers they feel they have come to understand a significant truth about how people are and what is going on in the therapeutic transaction. Such understanding is written of in the terms later accepted as the precepts of (say) psychodynamic counselling on the one hand or person-centred counselling on the other. Once published such schemes or descriptions may gain wider recognition and influence both because they are seen to tally with the experience of others who work in the field and because they are found to be effective in practice. Thus theoretical ideas are critically examined, refined in the light of further empirical use or research and perhaps developed by others who have an interest in the academic or scientific identification of what is happening in counselling.

Thus theory comes to mean what has been generally received as useful and constructive ways of describing the business of counselling. Counselling skills, within the definition we have described on pages 2–4, may be broadly linked to four different theories of counselling. These are person-centred, psychodynamic, cognitive and behavioural. Among these, the person-centred approach, mainly due to Carl Rogers, is central both in defining a counselling attitude and in providing a means for the helper to enable growth and change. The other theoretical stances offer alternative ways of responding to clients in order to challenge them in their experiencing or to help them systematically to identify goals and to begin to move towards them.

PERSON-CENTRED THEORY

Carl Rogers (for example, in *On Becoming a Person*, 1961) argues for the importance of his belief in the person as an entity and in their capacity for growth and change towards their full potential. Rogers identifies the individual person as unique. This means that there are no worthwhile generalised descriptions of 'how people are' that one can bring to counselling; to get to know and understand another person is only possible if one begins to perceive the world in the same way as he perceives it. Even the assumption that 'your experience is like my experience' (when rationally it may seem that way) is a dangerous one simply because at best that is all my experience can be – a similar experience, but still isolated in the person, place and time of its occurrence. At worst the assumption of similarity in its virtual absence – the act of labelling two very different experiences with the same label, be it 'giving birth' or 'facing death', may be inappropriate, misleading, even alienating unless the helper looks carefully and sensitively beyond the mere words. In the final instance, of course, the use of my experience to identify your experience is paradoxical; the best that can happen is that there is an agreement from both of us that the transaction in words spoken between us somehow represents a common understanding.

Nevertheless it is only through my experience of the world, awareness of my responses to it, through my use and understanding of language and through a process of abstraction from this that I begin to understand how you think and feel. Somehow I have to transcend my own experience to come to an understanding of the uniqueness of you! It is thus that Rogers describes the process of therapy as 'a deeply subjective existential experience in both client and therapist, full of complex subtleties and invoking many nuances of personal interaction' (1961: 226). To try to illustrate some of this effort to understand the other person's experience let us hear Karen, whose husband has recently left home to live with another woman, talking of her feelings to a social worker, Vicky.

> *Karen:* It's almost like the children didn't exist for him – he never makes any of the arrangements to see them, he never rings them or anything, yet I think he still wants to. . . . I feel he has betrayed us – and himself as well – does he really care or not?

Vicky begins to imagine how this must be for Karen. She tries to grasp some of the ambivalence of Karen's situation along with the hurt and resentment at her husband's treatment of herself and their children; she senses that Karen may have some belief in her husband, some compassion for him despite his behaviour. She tries to put this into words.

> *Vicky:* Even though he has turned his back on you all, causing all this upset and hurt, you still feel that part of him is trying to look in your direction – even to care for you?

Another central belief of Rogers is that each of us has the innate essential human capacity to grow psychologically and to change in ways which bring us closer to our real selves. He calls this the 'actualising tendency', implying a capacity within us to achieve our potential, to become what we are capable of becoming, even to transcend ourselves and the adverse events we experience.

So from a Rogerian point of view we might expect that Karen has the potential to cope with her loss and change of lifestyle; that this potential is realised in her relationship with Vicky; and that she is helped by Vicky's use of counselling skills to learn from this, to grow beyond it, taking on different attitudes, perhaps seeing the whole episode as a 'growth experience', part of her emergence as the unique person she is. Six months later Vicky may be saying to her:

Vicky: How do you see yourself managing in the future?

Karen: (*pauses*) I feel a lot stronger and more independent now – I don't have so much anxiety or depression about us coping and it's very useful having the outside contacts like the drop-in centre and the swimming group. Also I am beginning not to feel I am responsible for the children's relationship with their father. The way I see it, it has to be between him and them.

According to Rogers such growth and adjustment might have been anticipated as a direct result of the individual's essential capacity for self-enhancement and fulfilment. This he regards as a continuing inner dynamic assisted or hindered by the prevailing psychological environment, much as the growth of a plant is affected by its physical environment. Where adverse life events act against this growth causing traumatic or distressing consequences, raised defences or an unrealistic view of things, the process of adjustment and new growth may be achieved within a counselling relationship. Here the counsellor or professional helper tries to create the right conditions for this process to happen.

According to Rogers (e.g. 1961: 31) the essential conditions for this adjustment and new growth in a client to take place are provided in the attitude and approach of the therapist. He describes it as essential that the helper is: *real and genuine; respecting and valuing the client as a person; having a deep empathic understanding of the client's world in the way he (the client) experiences it.* These are sometimes called the 'core conditions' for counselling and they are important enough for me to allow them a little more explanation.

Theory and practice

Being real and genuine

This is seen as a kind of 'transparency' – a matching (or 'congruence' as Rogers calls it) of the counsellor's outward behaviour with her inner experience. She is aware of her own attitude and feelings and is prepared to reveal these, to 'be' these in her helping relationship. She is real, authentic, not pretentious, reserved or deliberately following a role or another prescribed way of behaving; she is, as best she can be, 'herself'.

Respecting and valuing the client as a person

It is not possible to like all of our clients. However, Rogers argues that we must recognise each client as a person, prize his uniqueness, respect his struggle to change and 'become himself', cherish his individual worth without preconditions or judgements. In the nursing profession a similar quality is 'tender loving care', commonly called 'TLC'. At the other extreme it may be more of the implicit knowing of another's human frailty because it so accurately reflects one's own, a theme which is powerfully and entertainingly illustrated in Sheldon Kopp's book, *If You Meet Buddha on the Road, Kill Him!* (1972).

Having empathic understanding of the client's world

As we have seen (p. 30), the helper has only her own limited experience with which to understand the client's world in the way he himself experiences it; to see things through his eyes and to refer to his frame of reference; to be able to sense his feelings and to begin to know his ways of responding. It is the means, deliberate or intuitive, by which the helper gets to know her client. This quality Rogers refers to as *empathy*. It is to be distinguished from *sympathy*, which is being simul-taneously affected with the same feeling as another person, sharing their emotion. The empathic helper is not so much sharing or experiencing her client's emotional responses (though this too can sometimes happen, and even then is not necessarily unhelpful), as sensitively recognising and inti-mately understanding them. Empathy is, as Rogers himself

43

has said, the adoption of a stance of gentle but confident companionship towards the client in his inner world.

Rogers' theory, therefore, offers the helper the means of growth and positive change for her client if the core conditions of respect, empathy and genuineness are maintained by her in the counselling relationship. As we have already seen in Chapter 2 it also argues for a steady focus on the experience of the client as he 'sees' it. This person-centred approach is present in all phases of counselling skills and Rogers' ideas have been a prime influence in establishing it. However, when we use challenging skills in an attempt to facilitate change (Chapter 2) we may be moving away from this person-centredness to a degree, moving more towards the helper's perception of the relationship, construction of circumstances or of the way the client is. Though we must not lose sight of the client-centred ways of working, it is important, too, to recognise that other theoretical approaches may contribute to and support the counselling skills model, especially in the important business of challenging. These arise predominantly from the schools of counselling or psychotherapy labelled as *psychodynamic, cognitive* and *behavioural.*

PSYCHODYNAMIC THEORY

As we have seen, challenges can come from the helper's awareness of the ongoing relationship between herself and her client. She feels it would be helpful to her client if she drew his attention to this, asking him to notice what is happening between them. She may also ask him to think about other relationships which connect with this, perhaps those with his own parents in childhood, believing that these early experiences will help him to understand some of the difficulties and confusions he has in the present. The psychodynamic theory underlying such beliefs is based on the following fundamental ideas.

Mental and emotional activity within us is either conscious (that is, we are aware of our thoughts and feelings) or unconscious (some mental and emotional processing happens without our being aware of it). Unconscious processes significantly and sometimes detrimentally affect the way we respond to current circumstances, for example by causing anxiety, distress

or defensive behaviour. These fundamental ideas are histori-
cally due to the thinking of Sigmund Freud (1856–1939) whose
influence extended well beyond his psychoanalytic theories of
human functioning and forms of therapy into the very heart
of western thought and culture in this century.

The purpose of psychodynamic counselling is to help clients
make sense of what is happening to them by enabling them to
bring into consciousness those things which are unconsciously
causing their difficulties. By recognising and better understanding these and by accepting the choice of acting independently of them, clients gain more control over their lives.

The personal history of the client, therefore, is of prime
importance and is assumed to be constantly reflected in the
here-and-now behaviour with the helper. In psychodynamic
counselling this is the transference which the client brings to
the counselling relationship (we have already referred to its
use in Chapter 2) and it may form the basis of further exploration later, for example in beginning to understand the unconscious and perhaps dysfunctional ways in which a client relates
to others, especially those who live close to them.

Thus Karen's social worker, Vicky, trying to help her deal
with her loss and her husband's ambivalent attitude towards
her and the children may be able to help her to be clearer
about how she related to her husband by examining their own
(worker–client) relationship:

Karen: One of the difficult things to cope with is why he
left me. I suppose he has found what he wants
with her, but what is it that she has that I haven't
got?

Vicky: What do you think that might be?

Karen: Perhaps she shows her affection more – I've
always found it diffcult to express my feelings to
Ian.

Vicky: And yet you seem to have been able to share your
feelings with me . . .

Karen: Yes . . . perhaps that's because you're a woman –
it feels like you expect me to, whereas with Ian,
now that I think about it, it felt as though he
didn't really want me to.

Vicky: So with Ian you felt somehow restricted in showing your feelings and you are wondering whether
that was just him or partly to do with what you
yourself expect men to be like.

The concept of client transference is an important one for all
helpers, even those who do not use counselling skills. Commonly the patient, relative, learner, client, resident or other
person cast in the role of 'helpee' has the expectation that he
will be helped, that the helper will somehow or other improve
his situation, solve his problems or create beneficial change of
some sort. The transference is that helpers in general can be
expected to help and that this particular helper will be of
special help in meeting needs and alleviating distress.

So far, so good. In practice, however, it may turn out that the
client, perhaps because of his own great need, has unrealistic
expectations of being helped; that the helper is cast in the role
of 'perfect parent' and to some degree idealised in her perceived
concern, investment and ability to change things. Her short-
comings, her failings, her lack of skill, indeed her very human-
ness are overlooked; more is expected from her than she can
give, perhaps more than anybody can give.

With such a strong positive transference of course she is set
up to fail, at least in the client's terms. And fail she does,
resulting in another and opposite transference (which one sus-
pects was around the corner all the time since and may well
relate to such an individual's early parenting patterns), the
negative transference, again associated with unrealistic expectations of what the helper can or should do. Thus our helper
sometimes finds that her client's distress turns into anger and
aggression directed at her. Her client sees his misfortune or
the failure to recover from it as her responsibility, her fault,
and unless she uses her counselling skills help him to deal
with this he will carry it away with him and into the next
situation where he is to co-operate with another person for
their mutual benefit. Perhaps it is more important here,
though, just to make the point that the anger and aggression
that many of us face from time to time from our clients may
be based on such a process of transference and does not necessarily mean the helper herself has been inefficient or negligent.

Such a sequence of events occurred in Vicky's visits to Karen.

At first Karen was hoping that Vicky would have enough knowledge and experience to get Ian, her husband, back home again. Even after several weeks she wanted Vicky to give her some reassurance that Ian still loved her and would eventually realise his mistake. Later she began to feel that Vicky was no help to her, indeed, had misled her and let her down when she most needed help.

Because Vicky had experience enough to contain this transference and to sustain her own empathic and supportive attitude through this more challenging period of their relationship, she was eventually able to help Karen to examine her own deeper feelings and attitudes, to understand some of the reasons why her marriage had failed and to begin to recognise ways in which she may have contributed to this.

The issues of the helper's own transference and counter-transference were discussed earlier. Realising that it might be helpful, Vicky told Karen of her own feelings about Karen's situation. Gradually, Karen became more aware of Vicky's attitude and opinions as representing a totally different approach to a marriage or partnership. Such challenges reflected Vicky's own beliefs in women's rights and they seemed to give Karen more strength and purpose in her gradual move towards independence of her husband.

COGNITIVE THEORIES

For a third perspective or theoretical support for the counselling skills model we turn to 'common sense' approaches – attitudes in the helper that challenge existing and often unrealistic or illogical thinking in the client. The two main contributors here are Reality therapy, due to William Glasser (for example, *Reality Therapy*, 1965) and Rational-emotive therapy, pioneered by Albert Ellis (for example, *The Practice of Rational-Emotive Therapy*, Ellis and Dryden 1987). These two approaches to counselling put a high priority on the cognitive processing – 'it's the way that you think that matters' is a central belief.

Reality therapy emphasises the importance of recognising reality – the way the world out there really is – in order to fulfil individual needs for worth and love and to achieve what Glasser calls 'a successful identity'. The helper draws attention to the consequences of client behaviour and helps him to choose ways of acting that are most likely to bring the result he needs to establish or re-establish himself in his life.

So Karen may be talking to Vicky about her continuing feeling of responsibility for her husband's failure to arrange to see their children. Vicky decides that it may be helpful to challenge that view, since, although Ian's departure could be seen partly as the result of Karen's behaviour, his continuing absence and failure to make contact with the children must be regarded as entirely his responsibility. There is nothing that Karen can do about this except to restate the conditions under which Ian's visits could be made and make it clear that she wants him to see the children. Acceptance of this fact means that Karen has more self-respect and feels less guilty about the situation she is in.

Rational-emotive therapy (RET) identifies and works on the primary connection between belief and feeling; that one's belief system largely affects the way that events are interpreted and consequently determines the feelings experienced. Thus one might view the glass as half-full or half-empty with the resulting feelings of satisfaction or regret according to which belief was held.

Ellis encapsulates this personal processing in his ABC model of response to events where:

A stands for *activating event* (usually some important and troublesome circumstance in the client's life) and the inferences that the client makes about this event.

B stands for client's *belief system*, especially in so far as it determines the evaluation he makes about A.

C stands for the *consequences* of A and B in this sequence, especially in the irrational thinking surrounding A and the dysfunctional feelings or distress that inevitably follow.

Especially important in the therapy is the identification of irrational beliefs, usually unnoticed by the client in his concern with the threatening activating event (A) and strongly experienced negative feelings (C). These irrational beliefs are often stated in absolute terms such as 'should', 'must', 'have to' and so on where such imperatives are neither logical nor necessarily shared by others in the situation. The therapeutic process therefore involves recognition of the relatedness of A, B and C, and acceptance of the responsibility for changing these by 'internally disputing' their logic or validity and by trying to replace them by more rational beliefs and more moderate emotions.

Let us re-examine Karen's distress at her husband Ian's departure, looking at it through an RET perspective. Karen's view of Ian's absence is the activating event (A). Among Karen's beliefs prevalent in the early months of his absence was that Ian still loved her and would eventually come back to her (B). The consequences (C) of this belief were that Karen continued to be hurt by what she saw as Ian's contradictory behaviour and that she was unable to move away from the position of being his victim and dependent on him for any improvement in her position. Vicky asked Karen to re-examine the beliefs and feelings she had about Ian, helping her to see how she was prevented from making changes and taking more control of her life by holding on to these. Karen gradually became more independent and more positive in her outlook on life, especially in coming to understand that her thinking and attitude towards Ian's leaving her did not have to be static and that she was in fact able to reduce her distress by taking some control over these.

BEHAVIOURAL THEORY

The final theoretical orientation that we have chosen focuses primarily on behavioural change. Behavioural psychology provides the basis for this in asserting the importance of *observable* behaviour, of attending to a person's actions and to the extent to which these are affected and controlled by the external world. Behavioural counselling adopts similar beliefs and the main features of its application to counselling skills are that it:

1 focuses primarily on specific ways of client responding, for example, in social interaction;
2 establishes goals to be achieved, the ways by which these are to be reached and the criteria by which they are to be assessed;
3 follows the principle that behaviours are reinforced by successful functioning or by achieving goals;

4 employs problem-solving techniques where these are appropriate.

We have already seen from Chapters 1 and 2 that the skills of planning action and change employ the above principles (see pp. 34–7) and in doing so provide a strategy for changing an unwanted situation in which the client is placed and simultaneously for reinforcing his own competency and self-advocacy.

A behavioural approach, particularly in the use of action skills, could also be of use to Karen in her need to cope more effectively with the dramatic changes in lifestyle caused by Ian's continuing absence. Perhaps the most important change is to begin to plan for a future without him. Vicky asks her to think about what goals she might aim at in this respect to be achieved in the next three months. When Karen says she wants to be more independent, Vicky asks her to say exactly what that would mean. By supportive questioning and clarification it is established that Karen will arrange to have swimming lessons for herself (she has never been able to swim!), will take the children away on holiday (supported by a single-parent group she has already joined) and will ask her brother and his wife to help her redecorate her bedroom. These are goals which meet the first two principles above and, when achieved will provide some of the self-assurance and comfort that Karen seeks, as well as the motivation to continue on the same road.

These, then, are the four most obvious theoretical stances to support the counselling skills model. There are others which the professional helper migh adopt or indeed may already be using, notably Transactional Analysis or Gestalt therapy, though these are more self-contained approaches and do not have the same obvious relationship to the counselling skills rationale that we are using.

DISCUSSION ISSUES

1 In his book, *Practical Counselling Skills*, Richard Nelson-Jones invites you to explore your theoretical preferences (1983: 219). One of six multiple-choice questions is as follows:

The best way to understand people is:

(a) to understand the way they see things
(b) to know what rewards are controlling their behaviour
(c) to understand the ways in which they think
(d) to explore their unconscious

With which of these statements do you tend to agree and with what kind of conviction if you do agree? How are such convictions – or lack of them – like to affect your approach to using counselling skills with your clients?

2 Think about Carol, Betty's patient on a surgical ward (pp. 27ff.) – or any other client that you have experience of. Consider how you might state her or his difficulty in person-centred, cognitive, psychodynamic and behavioural terms. Imagine how you might enable this client to make progress using each of these approaches or a combination of them as in the counselling skills model.

4

Self-awareness

WHAT IS SELF-AWARENESS?

Some years ago I was given a paper by a physiotherapist acquaintance and colleague about her work with people who were incurably ill or severely disabled or both. I had asked her to talk to my student physiotherapists about her own special way of working with these clients which seemed to owe more to her own experience of co-counselling (a form of self-help counselling in which two partners have similar training and a contract to share time equally) than to more orthodox physiotherapy. I was surprised to read at the very beginning of this paper, the statement: 'I start with myself.' It was my introduction to the idea of 'self as instrument'. As a teacher, coach, lecturer and group leader I had been familiar with 'self as actor', 'self as performer', 'self as informer', self as 'helper-agent' and so on, but not with the idea of using some kind of naked 'me', stripped of roles and labels, predetermined ways of functioning and other 'props'. Being me, being aware of me, deliberately promoting that awareness, internally referring to it and even using it with clients, was a personal insight I have always valued since reading those words and hearing what she had to say about them.

So, too, I have started with myself, and in this chapter, as a change for both of us, intend to go on using myself where possible as I try to explain what self-awareness is all about and why it really matters for users of counselling skills.

Even as a baby I have the capacity to interact with whatever and whoever is around me. I can think and feel about this experience and recall aspects of it when necessary. From this I begin to differentiate parts of my experience that refer to me and other parts which refer to the world outside of me. I understand that some things are 'me'; others are 'not me'. The beginnings of self-awareness exist.

In time and with maturity the process becomes more sophisticated as I learn more, have more widely varied experiences and start to see myself as others might see me. Indeed, one aspect of my growing self-awareness is that I am somehow defined by others, especially my parents, and I make strong attempts to resist this. Later still I become interested in psychology and begin to refer to myself in this study of how people in general are supposed to behave. Finally I am involved in counselling and am, as I have related, more acutely impressed with the idea of self-awareness as a key function in the counselling role.

So, too, will the professional helper have learned to work with some self-awareness when interacting with clients. In her counselling skills attitude she tries to understand the client's experience but is increasingly aware of how her own beliefs and feelings may affect this understanding.

In exploring the concept of self-awareness I notice my own need for some kind of structure and I refer to Philip Burnard (1989: 63) who names nine aspects of self-awareness and suggests methods of development in each: thinking; feeling; the senses; sexuality; spirituality; the physical body; appearance; knowledge; needs and wants. It seems a long list but as I type them out I notice that all have some relevance to me in my counselling. Aside from the more obvious ones of thinking and feeling, which I will talk more about later, there is the matter of my sexual attraction to some of my clients; also the intuitive spontaneous exchange that occasionally happens and seems to mean more than we can put into words – more perhaps than we can understand – is this spirituality?; then again I am also aware of my body, its condition, its position, my tired or failing eyes and my posture so frequently, it seems, mirroring that of my client. My appearance, too: what do they expect? (does it matter what they expect?); what do I want to say through my appearance?

I am aware, too, of knowing things, and of having skills, also of sometimes knowing very little or nothing about my client, and of course, because I know my own history, better and more intimately than before my spells in therapy, I am ready to recognise my reactions when they are mine and not necessarily connected to my client or to 'us'. Finally I am aware of some of my needs in the counselling relationship: to be accepted, recognised and respected; to be financially rewarded; to be challenged, to be committed, to learn and understand; to achieve and feel satisfied.

Inevitably, I guess, I am more aware of myself not only in the way I have been saying, that is in terms of *who I am, what I can do* and so on – the descriptive, labelled bits of me – but also of the moment by moment, 'stream of consciousness' experiencing of the here-and-now. Somehow, in the process of training, practising and helping others to learn, I am better at noticing myself, at watching and recording my internal functioning – the dynamic form of self-awareness as compared to the more static references I make to past experience.

Nevertheless this business of becoming more self-aware is and always will be an incomplete process. I will never be aware of everything that is in my unconscious and even if that were possible I cannot be outside of myself, as it were, to monitor the monitoring process. It is sufficient, perhaps, that I consciously and actively observe myself in the counselling, try to be honest in the face of difficulties and accept that the growth of self-awareness is a continuing process and one that increasingly liberates me to understand my clients more fully.

WHY IS IT IMPORTANT THAT I TRY TO BE MORE SELF-AWARE?

Good question! Because it is sometimes either taken for granted that one is adequately self-aware or it is treated as an affliction of self-indulgence among the helping professions that one should strive for this; yet again it may be resisted because gaining it is a process that threatens our defences and challenges well-established and comfortable ways of working. On the other hand in trying to explain what it is I have already littered the trail with clues about its importance.

In general, it is important that all those whose work involves making responsible interventions for the benefit of another person are aware of their own fitness and competence to do this. This awareness is simply expressed in the question 'Can I do this (immediate) work?' It means more, though: 'Am I competent, feeling fit, alert, prepared to take the job on and anticipating that I will be able to manage it without undue threat to myself or to my client?' Nor are these questions to be taken lightly. In today's climate of high unemployment, increasing role stress and job complexity, there are, in my experience, large numbers of care professionals who find it difficult to avoid compromise in some of these respects. Few of these are able to confront either themselves or their employers on quality of care issues, especially those involving their own feelings of pressure and stress, frustration and disillusionment, in case such confrontation leads to being seen as weak or as a trouble-maker.

A second and central issue for the counselling skills user is that of identifying the client and what he is, as distinguished from herself and what she is. The difficulty of using oneself to understand another, that is of being empathic in responding, has already been discussed (pp. 40–1). My task now is to explain the additional complication that inevitably influences my work with clients, that of my own transference as a worker. The transference, as we have seen (pp. 32–4 and 46–7) is a person's projection in the present relationship of attitudes, beliefs and feelings which are well established from past and often childhood relationships.

Sometimes I am insecure in my relationship with a client. I notice that I am anxious to demonstrate my competence, to obtain reassurance from my client that things are going well; on other occasions maybe I too easily look for an excuse to offer the client a way out of the work, because it avoids the possibility of my own failure. At the time some of this is achieved in ignorance of the possibility of it being my own transference. Further still from this awareness, I have good *reasons* for such behaviours. So it is important *for the client* that I appear competent, I tell myself (the client may not recognise competence when he sees it – usually clients are aware more of what is happening to themselves than how this is being achieved). It is a functional and sensible part of the counselling process that I ask my client how the session or sessions have been for him (I tell myself). Fair enough, but was this question put in a neutral and non-leading manner or did I hear myself saying 'Have you found this session to be helpful?' (reader, if you can't see the sense in this you need to go to the section on asking open questions on p. 23). So to the third example. Surely I am not prematurely showing people the door? Well, no, not exactly, but there was this instance of a *very* insecure client, terrified of counselling, whom I tried to reassure that she was free to leave at any time if her feelings of being trapped started to become overpowering! Now there is some sense in this if you attend only to the importance of client choice and autonomy. But here she is asking for help with this very dilemma and I respond by standing to one side when I might have encouraged her to stay with the feeling in this situation so that together we could work at the business of beginning to manage it.

All this is just one example of how growing awareness of one's own emotional past enables the helper to intervene more appropriately with her client. There are other examples that I might mention for you to think about. Giving more time than planned or agreed, giving 'extra' help or in general going out of one's way for a client are all evidence of the helper's own transference, whatever the emotions may be that lead to these behaviours. Similarly, the helper may be acting from any number of emotional responses promoted in her by her client, some of the less obvious of these being contempt, guilt, jealousy, fear of others' anger or disagreement, the need to protect and nurture others. The more obvious ones, perhaps, are to do with the counsellor's sexuality, her fear of failure, frustration about the client's lack of progress, or anger at the way he has been treated by somebody. It is important to repeat that while they are vaguely felt or in the helper's unconscious, such feelings get in the way, but that once they are revealed, usually in supervision or in the helper's own therapy, they may be put on one side or more deliberately used to the client's benefit. For example if I become aware that the client's over-apologetic manner irritates me then I can confront him with this, invite him to respond and to consider whether he promotes this feeling in other people, too.

Another important idea in this discussion is that of the 'wounded helper'. This draws my attention to the fact of my own dysfunction, deep-rooted needs and incompleteness which causes me to look in others for the unacceptable parts of myself. This is, in Freudian terms, called projection. As an example, I remember noticing that I became unreasonably angry at our children's untidiness with their toys and clothes, especially in not putting things away when they had finished using them. Then I realised that, in my own childhood, this had been my father's message to me and that my real anger and frustration was with myself in allowing this untidiness. Similarly as a helper there is a danger that I project my own needs for order and control on to my client so that I, rather than he, am assured of, say, 'satisfactory progress' or a 'plan to deal with the problem'.

As an unconsciously 'wounded helper' I have to put myself conspicuously in the 'sane', 'healed' or 'ok' categories, especially in contrast to my clients who are therefore in 'not ok' categories. The message here is that by becoming a 'helper' I am colluding with myself, as it were, to hide (from myself and others) my problems and deep-seated anxieties. By definition, my client is in one place and I am in another, whereas the reality is that, though we both have our troubles, we agree that for the moment I will put mine on one side in his interest. Not to recognise this means that I will mistake my problems for his, fail to be sensitive to and properly understand what is happening in him.

However, there is still another meaning to the 'wounded helper' concept and that is that I help my client to help myself. I profit by taking the credit for his success; by helping I become special, wanted, a valuable person, these labels having a kind of completeness, a wholeness in themselves. As Hawkins and Shohet explain in their important book, *Supervision in the Helping Professions*, I might try to think of myself as a *channel for help* and in doing so avoid the implications of attachment that the noun 'helper' carries, as well as the praise and blame that goes with it: 'Non-attachment does not mean not caring. On the contrary it may be the nearest we can get to real caring, as we do not have to live through our clients, dependent on their successes for our self-esteem' (Hawkins and Shohet 1989: 9).

THINKING AND FEELING

My experience tells me that thinking and feeling are simply different aspects of the same flow of consciousness; my feelings seem to be linked to the way I think and vice versa. Psychology tells me that the reception and appraisal of information *must* precede the emotional response; my distress can only come after I understand the bad news. Nevertheless my experience is of one happening and the division of it into two parts reflects more of western belief in the values of objectivity and science as a basis for acting than it does the understanding that the thinking/feeling (and for that matter, sensing, intuiting, spiritual, etc.) me, that is the *whole* me, is the one to attend to, to apprehend, to reckon with. And this is certainly so in using counselling skills. The danger is that when I begin to work with someone I collude with them in submitting to the cultural norms of being logical, objective and 'scientific', paying attention only to the 'story', the 'facts' of the 'truth' of the matter. In doing this I may overlook the very essence of their being: who individually, uniquely they are; how they are with me in this place; what is happening between us; and how I feel and observe myself responding. So it matters that I am aware of my tendency to think rather than to feel and that I remind myself to take a more open and receptive attitude to what is happening between us.

Of course, I have been trying to establish the importance of attending and responding to everything that another person is and perhaps, in the process, to correct a cultural imbalance by taking special notice of the feelings that are around. In doing so I do not want to devalue the importance of thinking, of classifying and identifying, of seeing connections between ideas and between events, of understanding, of imagining, of creating images and metaphors that illuminate and inspire both my client and myself to understand what we need to understand. Nor do I want to ignore the vital business of understanding at a meta-level, which is having a belief system about the counselling skills process, using theory which may well commit me to particular ways of working with my client.

I am aware of my own approach at this level; it follows fairly closely the ideas of Carl Rogers. This is because, when I read what he has written and when I see a film of him working it strikes me as having a special validity – the ring of truth about it. I think Rogers himself would have used the word 'resonates' to describe my experience, which statement illustrates the amount of influence he has had on me. Rogers' ideas about a person-centred attitude to clients also happened to reflect my previous experience of and commitment to child-centred teaching which was seminal in teacher training colleges and primary education where I was working in the late sixties.

However, my belief in Rogers' ideas was tempered by hard experience in joining a Marriage Guidance (now called Relate) agency where both training and practice led to the acceptance of other theoretical views and where I realised that the sheer volume of clients we were faced with demanded more active interventions and a constant search for quicker ways of helping people to deal with their difficulties. I became more pragmatic, using behavioural methods with some couples – after all, this was what they were asking for – that they could behave differently with each other. I tried, only half-convinced and, as I see it now, over-deliberately, to refer back to clients' own parenting to help them understand what was going on for them in their present. Then I learned that the basics of Transactional Analysis – an explanation of the ego-states, for example – seemed to help some clients to realise they had a choice in the way they behaved with others. Perhaps I had become what it is fashionable to describe as an 'eclectic' counsellor, but I still felt and do feel that my roots are in Carl Rogers' way of understanding things.

I have been illustrating self-awareness in my thinking as part of an explanation of self-awareness in general. I want also to say something about feeling as though it were a separate thing. It is feelings, not thoughts, that really determine the way I am, what I do. I do things to feel better and to avoid feeling worse. In this way I become who I am. Ronnie Laing illustrates such a process – referring, I think, to the growth of self-esteem – in his book of *Knots* (1970: 9)

> My mother loves me.
> I feel good.
> I feel good because she loves me.
>
> I am good because I feel good
> I feel good because I am good
> My mother loves me because I am good.

He then repeats the lesson for 'not loving' and 'feeling bad'. This is an important theme for many of us helpers. Are we 'good', lovable, acceptable to others? And if we are not, do we project those unacceptable bits of us out onto our clients?

Another aspect of feelings is prejudice towards certain groups of people in society; for example, women, ethnic groups, the elderly. In case you believed this was more to do with thinking and acting, let me remind you that deep down, underneath all that, perhaps buried out of sight and mind, is the fear, the dislike, the contempt for people in those groups. But then as right-thinking and responsible professionals, especially in using our counselling skills, we have dealt with all that, haven't we?

I went to a men's workshop which pursued the theme of men's oppression of women in our culture. It was led by John Rowan, who reminded us that prejudice existed at three levels: in our actions, which most of us who are interested try to do something about; in our thinking, which is probably a harder task but still partly within reach, I feel; and in our unconscious, which is almost impossible to deal with without some help. I feel, not least because I have a wife and three daughters, that I must try to deal with my own prejudices against women. I also felt, at the time of the workshop, that I had made a fair amount of progress in this respect. I had done a lot of thinking about it and had had useful contact with women who were in this context politically aware.

John asked us to close our eyes and to get into deep relaxation. He led us through a guided fantasy in which each of us was to be conceived, grow, be born as girls, develop and mature as women to experience the arrival and departure of fertility, and so on. I did not get very far before I made a painful discovery. I was born as a little girl . . . and I was *disappointed!*

THE GROWTH OF SELF-AWARENESS

So it seems a good idea that we, as professional helpers, do something about our degree or self-awareness in using counselling skills. This is partly because we want to be fit, understanding and skilful, partly because we want to avoid the limitations and hindrances, even dangers of not being self-aware and partly because we need to be experienced participants in, beneficiaries and living examples of the same process that we are offering to clients. It is only by working on our self-awareness that we can hope to become more genuine or transparent, more revealing of our inner selves to clients, a quality which Rogers says is likely to help promote therapeutic change in our clients.

As Rowan (1983: 58) points out, many writers both from psychodynamic and humanistic backgrounds have identified the difference between a central or real self and a peripheral or false self. In humanistic terms the counselling task is to get in touch with the real self which is obscured both by positive but phony, then negative, self-images as shown in Figure 5.

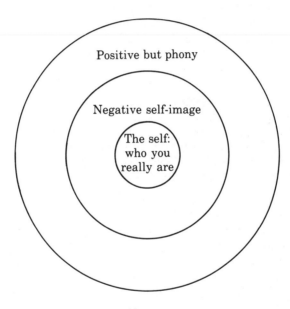

Figure 5 A humanistic picture of inner and outer selves (due to Rowan 1983: 59)

The outer area stands for the image we like to present to others for them to know us by. It is assumed both that this is false and that we know it is false. Underneath this we feel we are bad, unacceptable and needy, at the same time striving to present the more 'acceptable' us and failing to get in touch with or recognise a true inner self. The negative self-image is also false, however, and can be worked through to reach an 'ok' inner self.

As I said earlier (p. 41), one of the Rogerian beliefs is that this inner self is basically good and in the right conditions tends to grow and engage more in the world, in the form of a consciously fully functioning person, less defensive, more in touch with what is going on both inside and out. This process is called self-actualisation, and differs from self-awareness in that it implies an internal dynamic which constantly seeks to promote the inner self and prompt the whole person into finding individual ways of growing and expressing themself. How, then as professional helpers can we set about achieving greater self-awareness and personal growth, especially in relation to our use of counselling skills? The discussion issues that follow offer a start to this and I shall give more attention to it in Chapter 6.

DISCUSSION ISSUES

1 Self-awareness may be seen as combinations of knowledge about us held by ourselves and held by others. The 'Johari Window', originated by Joe Luft and Harry Ingham (1955), frames these combinations as follows:

	Known to self	*Unknown to self*
Known to others	PUBLIC	BLIND
Unknown to others	HIDDEN	UNKNOWN

One way to extend self-awareness, i.e., to get in touch with parts of the 'Unknown to self' boxes, would be to get feedback from others. Why is this a difficult process and how might such difficulties be overcome by people who want to learn more about themselves? What benefits and penalties arise from revealing more of your 'hidden' self? How could you find out more about the area which is labelled 'unknown' in the diagram?

2 Think about a colleague, client, friend or family member that you consider to be relatively self-aware. What is it

about this person that leads you to experience her or him as self-aware?

3   Choose any physical object either from where you are now (so that you can see it) or to picture in your mind's eye (something you are familiar with). Ask a partner to use her counselling skills to facilitate this exercise. Now describe the characteristics or qualities of this object, treating each quality as if it applied to you. For example, one might choose to describe a pin, referring each quality or thought to oneself: I am hard and shiny; I can prick and hurt people, but I can also be used for fixing things. What does 'hard' mean? . . . purposeful? . . . unrelenting?; what does 'I can prick and hurt people' mean . . . stimulate? . . . injure . . . accidentally or on purpose? . . . and so on.

5

Managing the Counselling Skills Process

INTRODUCTION

Given that our helper has sufficient skill and confidence to use her counselling approach for the benefit of her clients, there are still difficulties to be overcome. For example, colleagues' expectations may cause role conflict or threaten confidentiality. These and other 'surrounding' constraints we will call contextual factors. But there are still further potential difficulties and these are in the management of the counselling process itself, for example in providing openings, giving time, contracting, etc., all of which have to do with the face-to-face interaction between helper and client. We will first consider the contextual factors, then the management of the process itself.

CONTEXTUAL FACTORS

Role conflict

From what we have seen of Jan, the district nurse, Angela, working in residential care and Betty, on a hospital ward, or any member of the professional care groups named at the start of this book, it is clear that as they work with a particular client they have to make judgements about what kind of response is most appropriate at any one time. For instance, it was stated on page 4 that helping responses may be categorised into direct action, giving advice, teaching and counselling. Broadly these can be divided into two modes: authoritative and facilitative (Heron 1986: 12). Direct action, giving advice and most aspects of teaching are authoritative, that is to say the helper's intervention depends on her objective and factual knowledge of the client's situation, her skills, her understanding of what is going on, her experience of similar instances and her decision about what is the best thing to be done. On the other hand some aspects of teaching and most approaches to the use of counselling skills are facilitative. This means the interventions are made in such a way as to emphasise and enhance the wisdom, understanding, awareness, authority and actions of the client. Logically these two ways of responding tend to exclude each other. One cannot decide what action is best for the client and simultaneously promote his decision if it happens to be different. In the helping process, therefore, it is important that the helper consciously recognises whether she is working authoritatively or facilitatively, and that she is able to make and sustain the change from an authoritative to a facilitative way of working with her client despite the fact that most of her previous work experience has been more authoritative than facilitative. Thus when she adopts a counselling skills approach, presumably because of what her client has introduced into the interaction between them, she mentally changes hats; she is aware of a different way of responding; her attitude now begins to emphasise the importance of her client's thoughts, feelings and actions; she is not analytic, diagnostic and prescriptive; she becomes a catalyst, an enabler, an acceptor, a promoter of her client rather than herself as having the power and the means to change; essentially, too, she stops taking responsibility for the client in ways that she may previously have done.

It is possible that the client is not ready for such a change of attitude. Many clients do not automatically or necessarily expect a counselling skills sort of response from their helpers. Much depends on the circumstances, previous meetings and how things have developed up to this point. If our client sees us as a source of great knowledge and wisdom (a perception we ourselves may have helped to create) – as in the example given in the section on transference (p. 33) then there is obviously some kind of difference in our mutual expectations of each other; this is role conflict.

For example, Allen, a physiotherapist, has been treating

Brian, a 52-year-old-stroke patient, for eight months, trying to help him recover the use of the left side functions of his body; he can do nothing much with his left arm and can only just use his left leg to support himself; he cannot walk without considerable support. However, little improvement is now being made and Brian, becoming frustrated and angry with this, blames Allen for his failure to progress. At this point Brian's expectations of Allen are focused more on his abilities as a physical than a psychological therapist. Allen himself takes a broader view of things, knows that a full recovery is unlikely and recognises Brian's frustration as something he can help him to deal with. He responds to Brian's angry accusation that he is 'falling down on the job' not with an explanation of the physiological effects of the stroke or the aims and scope of the physiotherapy treatment, but with a statement about feelings: 'I can see you are upset about your lack of progress – I would be, too, in your position – it must be very difficult to keep trying when nothing much seems to happen.' In this way Allen has moved the focus from himself to his patient, established their separateness in the relationship (though referring sympathetically to his own feelings) and has opened up the possibility of discussing Brian's feelings more fully, perhaps enabling him to recognise and begin to accept that further progress is increasingly unlikely as time goes on.

This example again illustrates the basic difficulty for helpers who use counselling skills: that clients may expect them to act in such a way as to conform with their main and designated roles. Teachers are expected to teach, nurses to provide nursing care, social workers to help with family problems and so on. Clients are not primarily or perhaps in any event expecting their helpers to discuss their feelings or more personal aspects of their future or how they themselves may come to terms with this. Neither are they automatically receptive to a sudden change from an authoritative to a facilitative attitude. Such an about-face has to be accommodated either in the ongoing style or manner of the helper which clearly anticipates a shared responsibility for what is happening, or is directly negotiated when the helper herself makes such a change. For example, when faced directly with a question about what he, the client, should do about, say, a delicately poised social problem she might say, 'Now we are talking about things that you know much more about than I do' or 'I feel that's a question that you must try to answer for yourself' or 'Perhaps we could look at that together'.

Another related source of role conflict is between the helper and her employing agency, organisation or managers. While she sees her own use of counselling skills as the most appropriate way of working with her client at that time, it may be that her employers do not. Counselling skills may be seen as an 'optional extra' rather than as an integral part of the job, or worse still, as an unnecessary waste of time when there are more 'objective' and visible tasks on hand. The use of counselling skills as part of a job which is not that of counsellor is easier for the helper when she is recognised as doing this, when such recognition is written into her job description and when the implications of such acceptance, such as supervision, high levels of confidentiality, privacy and so on are acted on to ensure the appropriate conditions for such work.

The extent to which this happens at present is greatly variable. What follows are excerpts from the job descriptions of qualified professionals, all of whom have a substantial counselling skills function in the practice of their work:

'to offer an advice, guidance and counselling service for young people.'   (Youth service worker)

'to maintain and develop a ... pre-operative and post-operative ... programme which is responsive to the physical, social, *psychological* and educative needs of the ... patient.'
(Rehabilitation nurse; my italics to mark the
closest reference to counselling skills)

'to provide information and counselling where appropriate with respect to friendship, personal and social relationships.'
(Part of one of several key tasks for support
worker for residents with learning difficulties)

'to advise on the needs of pre-school children and to offer parental counselling in individual cases.'
(Team leader of a service for children
with visual impairment)

Several other workers, personally known to the author to be making regular use of counselling skills as part of their work, were contacted before this was written. None had reference to counselling or counselling skills in their job descriptions. These included a music therapist, residential social worker, school nurse and teacher in special education.

Counselling skills, therefore, are not always a well-defined or established part of the helper's work, even when they might be appropriately and effectively used. Perhaps this is because, increasingly, helping organisations understand the implications of the term 'counselling' and are reluctant to write it in unless its implementation can be fully justified and properly established. The term 'counselling skills', as implying the use of a counselling attitude as part of the work designated by a different job title, is not yet prevalent among the various people-orientated and managerial professions either. Indeed there is still some dispute between counsellors, even within the BAC itself, as to what counselling skills does mean, notwithstanding the position that was argued in the opening chapter of this book. All this presents either ambiguity or conflict for the helper who may be making an informed and adaptive effort to do her work effectively by using counselling skills as part of the work.

Availability

Obviously helpers need to have or to create time to help clients by using their counselling skills. Despite the evidence just presented, many professional disciplines in health, social and medical care include some training in or acknowledgement of the use of counselling skills within the work. Nurses, community carers, occupational therapists and physiotherapists, and especially all of the foregoing who have a psychiatric function are significant examples of this within the health professions; residential workers, social workers, teachers (perhaps more of those working with groups who have special needs) are also prominent examples; in industry those whose responsibilities connect with the health and welfare of the workforce, such as staff establishment, personnel and occupational health workers as well as line managers, are increasingly represented as using counselling skills (for example, Reddy 1987). In most of these instances the counselling skills function relates to the emotional and social disturbance incurred by the primary and explicit reason for the contact with the helper, such as illness, injury, accident or loss; in the remainder, such as line manager, there is recognition of exceptional and threatening circumstances that occur in all our lives from time to time, for example, financial difficulties, relationship problems, possible redundancy.

In all these professional uses of counselling skills there has to be a recognition of the time, degree of competence and commitment that is needed for the work to be effective. The helper has to be available, to make a judgement about the importance of using counselling skills in comparison with other work she may have to do, and then to communicate her availability to her client. All of this, too, has to be acceptable and supported practice within her work organisation.

Andrea, for instance, is a rehabilitation nurse on a coronary care unit in a large hospital. Her work includes liaison with ward staff and doctors, visits to wards, setting up and facilitating patient groups and using advice, information-giving and counselling skills either on the ward or in her own office with individual patients. Her establishment in this variety of roles is supported by other staff, her immediate and senior managers and a supervisor with whom she discusses her work with patients. Her patients may be referred to her by other staff or become involved during a ward visit. Typically Andrea will introduce herself to a patient as a rehabilitation nurse, explain that she is there to help them to understand some of their problems and to deal with any worries they may have, telling them how she may be contacted and where she works. To do a job like this she needs to have the freedom to plan her work independently to the extent that she can meet patients at short notice if this is what is needed.

Intimacy

It may surprise some readers that intimacy is included in a list of considerations that are seen to affect the management of the counselling skills process. The reality is that the intimacy of some professional interventions promotes the sharing of personal information, just as in turn the use of counselling skills also creates a climate of intimacy. An important form of intimate communication is touching and touching patients or clients forms an integral part of many health care treatment and therapeutic routines. Health professionals and lay people alike see various instances of bodily contact primarily aimed at treating, diagnosing, assisting, guiding and so on as *additionally communicating ideas and feelings* to the patient, typically as showing care and concern towards him (for example see Pratt and Mason 1984). Patients respond to this expression of respect and empathy by being more open, perhaps revealing their feelings. Nurses often report that it is during bathing that patients choose to say more about themselves and their worries.

Part of the same situation, of course, is that intimate bodily touching often requires the privacy of a separate room, cubicle or curtained area and therefore the privacy, too, encourages the patient or resident in his self-disclosure. The fact that nobody else is present and that the helper is seen as personally understanding and trustworthy constitute an opportunity for the client to say what is on his mind.

Sometimes an 'incidental' exchange of this kind can lead into a more formal opportunity to use counselling skills with clients. Time may be limited for either or both parties and it may be seen as preferable to delay the discussion until a mutually more convenient occasion can be found. On the other hand, say in residential care, a worker may have regular 'talk time' contracts with residents for the purpose of private, more intimate conversations which focus on the resident's concerns and do so by means of a counselling skills approach. The business of making and arranging such opportunities for the purposeful use of counselling skills is discussed on pages 79–80.

Confidentiality

Role conflict and physical intimacy affect the counselling skills response, then; so too do other conditions which contribute to a climate of trust and openness. Chief among these conditions are confidentiality, privacy, comfort and relaxation. The first of these, confidentiality, is an important issue in almost all work with people and the counselling profession in particular has recognised the special significance of this in strenuous efforts to secure high standards in its work with clients. The

BAC, for example, published its *Code of Ethics and Practice for Counsellors* in 1990; it has also published a *Code of Ethics and Practice for Counselling Skills* (1989). It is of obvious benefit to clients if helping professionals work to these standards and make it clear to all concerned that they are doing so. The BAC refers to confidentiality as 'a means of providing the client with safety and privacy. For this reason any limitation on the degree of confidentiality offered is likely to diminish the usefulness of counselling' (British Association for Counselling 1990: B.4.1). The BAC *Code of Ethics and Practice for Counselling Skills* refers the user to any agreement about confidentiality she may make with her client, which should itself be consistent with any written code governing her 'functional role', in other words her professional and/or organisational ethics and codes of practice.

Confidentiality is both a contextual and a counselling skills process issue. Its preservation depends on the rules and/or codes of practice at the organisation she works in. Of course, it also depends on the way in which the helper handles the work with her client when they are together.

The fact that a client may be located within a setting which exists for a purpose ostensibly other than intimate discussion of his concerns or for some kind of counselling activity militates against the preservation of confidentiality, even though this is highly desirable and indeed striven for. The common business within a hospital, school or residence often means that information about one person is widely spread around. This being so, it is difficult to confine the more confidential aspects just to those immediately concerned.

For example, in a teaching establishment, a member of staff, through her use of counselling skills, is able to help a student or resident on a one-to-one basis. She becomes aware of the student's high level of distress which is having a major impact on his capacity to take a full part in and benefit from the programme he is offered. It is desirable that other members of staff know something of this in order that they can make some allowance in their joint work with the individual. Again, illness or injury often throw into sharp relief other highly charged aspects of a patient's life – say an extreme commitment to a business or career, or a problematic marriage relationship. In such cases it may be in the patient's best interests that others have some knowledge of this. Different kinds of assistance may be available; staff can take a more expansive and understanding approach to this person and in some cases be prepared to adapt according to his needs.

In each of these situations it is important not to break an actual or implied offer of confidentiality and if it is thought to be to the client's advantage to do so then this must be discussed with him before anything is said to others. Further than this a helper should identify with her client the people to be told and the information that is to be given to them. Here is an example: Stephanie, a school teacher, has discovered that one of her students, Mark, who is 14, feels angry, confused and rejected because his father has left home to live away from the family. He is now questioning the use or purpose of being at school and of working towards examinations which all the family had previously thought was important. To Mark it all seems pointless and he wants to leave as soon as he can. Meanwhile he is often away from school, spending time with other truants in the town or at one of their homes. Stephanie thinks it is important that other teachers know how Mark feels at this time and why he is not always at school.

Stephanie: Mark, now that you have told me about your father, I think it would help both you and other teachers if you were to allow me to tell them about your situation too.

Mark: But you said this was just between you and me!

Stephanie: I know I did and it still will be if you want it that way, but I do believe it would help if Mr Knowles and Mrs Forsythe at least knew how difficult things are at the moment. They would understand that you hadn't been letting it all go without a good reason and they could make some allowance for that in the future.

Mark: I don't think there is much future for me.

Stephanie: Well, you may not feel very positive, but some of us still think it's worth a try – that's why I want these two teachers to know.

Mark:	OK, but I definitely don't want all of 3T gabbing about this.
Stephanie:	Of course; I believe that Mr Knowles and Mrs Forsythe would respect that.
Mark:	All right then ... if that's what you think is best.

In more pressing circumstances Stephanie felt she was bound in her student's interest to break her agreement to confidentiality with her. She had been spending some time with Sharon after an incident in which Sharon and another girl were reported for sexually molesting a third girl in the P.E. changing room. Sharon found it very difficult to admit this and after two half-hour sessions with her Stephanie was gaining her confidence and beginning to hear the full story. Sharon suddenly disclosed that her father was always after her sexually, trying to corner her in the same way that she had tried to 'get' the girl in the changing room. When she described in more detail exactly what her father was doing and how long this had been going on for, Stephanie felt that, as a teacher, and acting legally 'in loco parentis' (i.e., as a 'good parent'), she would have to tell her head teacher about this and that others may eventually have to be told as well. Sharon was aghast and then became very upset, demanding that Stephanie told nobody as she had promised to do previously. Stephanie was now in a no-win situation, having to go ahead with what she felt was her moral duty and risk losing the trust she had built up with her student. In fact she did discreetly and responsibly inform her head about this and managed to maintain her supportive relationship with Sharon through the ensuing very distressing period for Sharon and her family.

Helpers are faced sometimes with situations where they judge confidentiality has to be breached to ensure the safety of their client or others. Absolute confidentiality is not possible within most helping activities. For example, counsellors and counselling skill users are usually supervised, which implies the possibility of bringing a description of the client, his situation and details of the conversation with his helper, although anonymously, to a third party. Therefore it is better to explain some of this to the client in advance. Stephanie might have said to Sharon at the beginning of their talks together: 'I am hoping that by talking, you and I will be able to sort things out together. I must tell you now though that sometimes I hear things from children – perhaps to do with their safety, for example – that I feel I must get help with from somebody else. This does mean that occasionally I can't keep everything that is said just to myself.'

It is also possible that Stephanie might have anticipated that Sharon was going to tell her about the abuse just before she actually did so or before the full story was revealed and could have said something similar at that time, giving Sharon the choice of continuing or not. This does seem like passing the buck at the last moment, though, at a time when perhaps it is Stephanie and not Sharon who is better able to contain the situation.

When circumstances seem to the helper to be serious enough for her to consider breaking her undertaking to keep a confidence it is appropriate to:

1 seek the client's agreement to tell other persons, as the helper sees it, in his interest. If this cannot be obtained and it is still thought necessary to inform a third party or parties, tell the client exactly what and who is to be told;
2 consult with her supervisor, manager or experienced colleague to discuss the implications of doing so (if possible without referring to the specific case);
3 restrict both the amount of information given and the number of people informed to a minimum;
4 assure the client of the helper's continuing support for him despite the fact that he may feel betrayed by the helper's action.

Privacy

It is only possible even to begin to maintain confidentiality if the meeting is not witnessed or the conversation is not overheard. One drawback of having a 'counselling room' in a school, factory or residence is that others may see two parties entering or leaving and draw their own conclusions. If counselling skills are to be used in the course of helping clients to deal with their own intimate thoughts and painful, even unfaceable feelings; if distress, anguish and confusion are to be expressed and owned;

if secrets never before revealed are to be told; tears long with-held released; and crippling burdens slowly disengaged and put aside, privacy is essential.

Privacy means finding a place to work where one cannot be seen or heard by others. Obscured windows will prevent visual identification of what is going on and walls that muffle the sounds of distress as well as dialogue will help. Again it is preferable that a private room for counselling skills users is removed from general traffic and day-to-day operations; so too, the use of the manager's office may have connotations of authority and discipline for a client who is also an employee. Clearly, places like the ward, the day centre, the common room, even though offering curtained or screened areas, are a poor makeshift for real privacy and are certain to restrict the client's confidence and freedom in telling of himself. Some organisations do put aside small rooms for confidential and business meetings and this practice is closer to meeting the conditions needed. Preferably there should not be a telephone in the room and it should be possible to avoid other intrusion or interruption either by warning others or using a 'Do not interrupt' notice.

Comfort and relaxation

Even if some degree of privacy is secured we need to look further to see that our client is as comfortable and relaxed as possible in the circumstances. The intimacy of some situations, such as bathroom or treatment cubicle to which we referred earlier, may help this. Another contributing factor is the personality and interpersonal skill of the helper as she sets up the interview. Her own familiarity with and confidence in the situation will encourage her client as will her sense of purpose in attending and responding to immediate concerns and her ability quickly to establish an empathic relationship.

The physical surroundings matter, too. Privacy enables people to feel more at ease and we can try to add to this. With ambulant clients, comfortable easy chairs are a useful start; being at a similar level is also important, especially to see that the helper's head is not higher than that of her client. Chairs which are opposite each other suggest a purposeful and focused atmosphere, while chairs at right angles imply a more casual attitude; either may be appropriate. Some helpers like to begin an interview with a cup of tea or coffee. It is probably more of a handicap than a help because the social ritual of nurturing and sharing (both positive assets in building a relationship) may obscure or detract from the more important task of addressing the client's concerns. It is better to avoid the distraction and get down to business, which in most cases is more important to the client than drinking tea!

If the client is bodily disabled, in bed or chairbound, has loss of vision or hearing, some of these considerations go by the board and the helper has to position herself in an adapted relationship. Her client, having more experience of the problem, may be able to tell her where and how she should set things up for their mutual benefit. The main consideration is that communication is as unrestricted as possible so that both parties can optimally understand each other. The helper has to strive to preserve this and indeed on some occasions, when clients have difficulties in speaking or understanding, to struggle for even a small amount of it. In such instances the medium does almost become the message in much the way that Carl Rogers maintains that the core conditions themselves are of therapeutic value; the fact of establishing a mutual understanding has its own moving influence in promoting the client as a person and enabling him to use his own power to grow and change.

MANAGING THE COUNSELLING SKILLS PROCESS

We have just considered a number of ways in which the helper is constrained or occasionally assisted by what we have called contextual factors. Now we are to look at how she manages the face-to-face process itself. Here again we shall find that there are special aspects of that process arising from the fact that the helper is not a designated counsellor and is not necessarily seen by her client as using a counselling attitude or approach.

Figure 6 is a flow chart and contains a sequence of questions that the helper may find it useful to ask herself about her use of counselling skills. The sequence runs from top to bottom of the page, representing an order of happenings corresponding to the helper's experience in her use of counselling skills. We

General question	Specific question
Do I use counselling skills?	Is the use of counselling skills appropriate?
Shall I give time?	Where? When?

Is there a   Now?
suitable/   Later?
private   For how
place?   long?
↓

| *What can I offer?* | How do I begin? (How do I end?)
↓
What kind of (counselling skills) help does my client want from me?
↓
Can I give this help? (Do I have the understanding, skills, resources?) |

↓   ↓
                              No!
What is our contract?   ↓
(e.g. timing, frequency of   Refer?/
meeting, confidentiality)   Consult?
↓

How is it going?	Am I coping? How do *I* feel? How well did I do? What am I expecting of myself? ↓ Have I managed time appropriately? ↓ Does my client feel I have helped him? What next? ↓
What supports and constraints do I have?	What does my organisation expect of me in a counselling role? ↓ Where do I get my supervision/support from? ↓ What further training do I need?
What else should I be thinking about?	

Figure 6 Managing the counselling skills process

will look at the questions in the top half of the figure in this section leaving the remainder for the next chapter.

Do I use counselling skills?

Without an explicit reference to counselling (which is not necessarily precluded and may be helpful to indicate to the client the kind of help that is on offer) the use of counselling skills tends to arise from the client's expressed or implied need. He says he would like to talk about a concern or he expresses feelings, say of anxiety, anger or distress that seem to call for recognition and understanding. Counselling may arise from the helper's observation, inference or intuition that something is wrong and she should somehow reveal that she knows or senses this. In some instances, typically when a client breaks into tears, it is a counselling skills response that is needed. In others the helper may have a choice in the way in which she responds to her client, perhaps, as in the following example, deciding to leave her own planned work with the client in order to pick up what seems to be more important for him.

Mac, a patient on a ward for the elderly is to be discharged tomorrow and Frances, an enrolled nurse, is talking through some of the more important things he will need to do when he is back at home. She begins by remarking that she expects that Mac will be looking forward to getting home. Mac says: 'Well, no, not really. Since Eleanor died there's nothing for me to go back for – the truth is I'm dreading it.' Frances looks at her schedule of questions about discharge, wondering whether to go on with the next point. After a little thought (and a few seconds of silence) she puts her clipboard down and says: 'Yes, life must seem pretty empty when there is no one at home to share your day with', again pausing to show that she is ready if Mac wants to say more about this.

On the other hand the helper may notice a client's or colleague's unfamiliar disposition, such as unusual silence, obvious disquiet or over-reaction to another's statement. She may decide it is appropriate to make an offer to talk about his demeanour. In the spirit and practice of a person-centred approach this offer is made in such a way that it can be refused as easily as it can be accepted, as these examples indicate.

'You've been very quiet today, Bob, is there something on your mind?'

'How are things with you, Ruth?'

'I get the impression that you're not happy with the new set-up, Peter – would you like to talk it through with me?'

It is just as important to accept a 'no' answer without further probing as it is not to manipulate the client into saying something against his better judgement in the first place.

Part of this opening dialogue might also refer to the end to find a more appropriate time and/or place to meet. We have already discussed the suitability or otherwise of various environments for counselling skills interviews; giving and using time is what we now explore in more detail.

Shall I give time?

The question of whether and when to give time again highlights the role conflict created by the use of counselling skills. Unprotected by the clear boundaries that are established by her counsellor equivalents in professional practice (for example in having an appointment system and a fixed length of time, often one hour, for the counselling session), she usually has to make an *ad hoc* judgement about such considerations. Clients present their concerns when the time is right for them or when, as they see it, an opportunity presents itself. The timing of these expressions may or may not conflict with the helper's other work in hand or planned for the day. She, perhaps as a community nurse, may be expected to make another call in thirty minutes, yet her present client's emotional upset demands, in her opinion, more time with him than she had previously scheduled. If she does spend another twenty or thirty minutes with this client now, she will have to justify this to herself, to her other patients and to her manager. In the present climate of cost-cutting the management focus is frequently on more measurable objectives, such as visits completed, treatment given and the like, rather than on the quality of care that results from appropriate and sensitive use of counselling skills.

On the other hand time does need to be explicitly managed.

The attitude that one will give 'as long as it takes' is seldom to be adopted and then probably for exceptional circumstances (such as a threatened suicide or intention to injure) until other help can be called upon. It is good practice to agree with the client that a certain length of time is available to both helper and client, either now or later. This means that both parties can make the best use of that available time, the client, understanding that time is limited, says what is most important for him. A proviso that further time might be needed on another occasion is preferable to drifting on without or beyond an agreed time.

Another possible scenario is that in spite of the client's clearly demonstrated need for help at the present time, it is imperative that the helper deals with other business or attends a previously arranged appointment. It must be emphasised here that although delaying discussion of the concern to a later time or date may be unsatisfactory for both people, it still has merit. The offer of further help and the assurance of an agreed occasion on which the matter will be faced together, in short that the concern has been recognised and carried forward, all contribute to an easing of the client's anxiety and to the building of a productive relationship.

What can I offer?

How do I begin? (How do I end?)

The third heading, 'What can I offer?' in Figure 6 leads to five questions, the first two of which are about beginning and ending a counselling skills session. The question of how to begin is partly pre-empted by what was said under 'Do I use counselling skills?' Notwithstanding this there will be occasions when the helper has no notion of what is coming from her client other than that he wants to talk to her. If she feels a lead from her may be helpful she may try to refer to what she knows or thinks about her client, even though this may not turn out to be his concern; for example: 'You seem not to be your usual self lately John', or referring back to a previous meeting: 'You were saying yesterday how worried you were about going for surgery.' More usually, though, she may choose to use a general open question to start things going: 'What's worrying you, Adam?'; 'What did you want to talk to me about, Bethy?'; 'Can you tell me about the difficulty/problem/worry, Charles?' or simply 'How can I help you?'

Another alternative is not to offer a lead or a question, but simply to give full attention to the client while maintaining silence, in the expectation that the client will explain himself and his concern. This also avoids the possible difficulty of leading him away from what may be most important for him. But an extended silence may not be helpful either, so even then the counsellor may choose to make a 'here and now' statement (see the section on immediacy, p. 32) such as 'You are finding it difficult to start', or 'Maybe you're wondering where to begin', in order to avoid more acute difficulty for her client.

Endings, too, need to be directly addressed. If, as has been suggested, some agreement is obtained on the length of time to be used, then both client and helper are ready for an appropriately made ending and the actual conclusion is correspondingly easier to manage. In any case it is the helper's responsibility to manage the time and she will have to refer to the ending when it is near or imminent: 'I see we have about five minutes left', 'That's all we have time for right now', 'I will just remind you that I have to go in ten minutes, because earlier you said you wanted to talk about so-and-so and you haven't mentioned that yet' or 'I know this is going to be difficult for you, but we must finish here – perhaps we could arrange to meet again in a day or so?'

What kind of (counselling skills) help does my client want from me?

Yet again this question puts into sharp focus the possibly ambivalent nature of the counselling skills exchange. Where the counselling skills episode begins, as it may often do, with the client's experience and expression of strong emotions, he probably does not know what he wants from the helper, nor how he might, in the course of a supportive conversation, achieve some kind of change for the good. The expression of anxiety, distress or anger is spontaneous; initially, the client may not have thought about how this should or could have been allowed to happen or what it will lead to. However it is assumed that the helper has enough understanding, skill and confidence to accept and work with these feelings. After a time her client experiences the benefit of this and begins, himself, to understand, anticipate and even to control the counselling process and more consciously use the skills and persona of the helper.

Of course there are other occasions when clients intend to talk about particular worries with their helpers, perhaps expecting that they have an 'answer' to what realistically has no objective solution. Clients hope that there is some aspect of the problem that is yet uncovered, that there is a cure for their distress just as medicine can alleviate physical ailments; a way of altering their oppressive circumstances, of bringing a lost partner or child back into the family that they may have overlooked; even hope for some miraculous power in their helper. The immediate business of a counselling skills response in such circumstances is first fully to hear this expectation and to communicate that it has been heard and understood; this is clearly to establish both for helper and client that that is what he thinks and feels. 'So you feel it is *Mike's* fault that you are landed with this' or 'What *you* are hoping for is that I will be able to sort this out for you'. Then, as the foregoing examples imply, without colluding in any false or unrealistic belief that the client appears to hold, the helper may use a sensitive challenge in the manner already described (pp. 24–34).

The two preceding paragraphs relate to situations where it is implied that the clients do not know or are not sure about what their helper can offer in the way of what she herself would call 'counselling skills'. It is wrong to assume that all clients are like this. Some will recognise the care and under-standing of their helper and will also be conscious of their own need to talk about or talk through their feelings and concerns. In these cases the client is more consciously ready to engage in and use the counselling process, thus releasing the helper from the kind of ambiguity of expectations that we have so often encountered before.

Can I give this help? (Do I have the understanding, skills, resources?)

Part of the helper's function in the counselling skills process is to monitor and review what is going on between her client and herself, to establish a 'fly on the wall' perspective of the counselling skills process, to try to decide whether the intervention is helpful to the client and to notice how she herself is living with the experience. For example, part of her should be alive to her own anxiety in the relationship, to the doubt, worry or oppression she feels from or in the process, to the possibility of failure or rejection by her client. She may also feel recognition, acceptance, commonality of purpose, pleasure, worthiness and satisfaction, even delight at what is happening. All of these responses and other more detailed impressions of what is said and heard are to be carefully and thoughtfully monitored as they occur. Later, perhaps reflecting on all this as she writes some account of the proceedings, she will adopt a more separate or distant perspective; later still in discussion with her manager or other work consultant her different perceptions and feelings about the counselling skills session will be reviewed again, perhaps achieving new awareness of or insight into what has taken place (see p. 98).

So the question 'Can I give this help?' is one that has to be put into a wider context than that of first impressions or even, perhaps, one meeting with the client. Seldom is it a question that requires a final answer 'yes' or 'no' – unless it is an obvious 'no' at the outset for reasons that the helper herself is very clear about. More often it is one we should keep continually at the front of our minds. Perhaps the question itself should be redrawn in more permissive tones, so that we do not needlessly and prematurely jump into flight just because the going looks a bit rough. So, instead of the original closed question implying a 'yes or no' we could more profitably ask open questions of ourselves such as: 'In this interview, how can I enable the client to get what he wants or needs?'; 'What understanding, skills and confidence do I have to sustain the process?'; 'If I lack some or all of these, what could I do about it?'; 'What additional resources are immediately available to me?'; 'What is it that I find in this client that make me doubt my own abilities to work with him?'

These questions draw attention more precisely to the nature of a challenging or difficult relationship with a client than does the original one ('Can I give this help?') and are therefore less likely to result in an instant withdrawal from the counselling skills role.

This is especially important for those helpers who are inexperienced or unconfident in their use of counselling skills. As we have noted, the use of counselling skills produces demands and ambiguities around the role which, together with difficulties or doubts about the process itself, may well persuade the helper to abandon her counselling role for her better defined and perhaps more acceptable nominal role, for example, to return to the familiar and more objective tasks of nursing, paramedics, education, residential care and so on. The professional helper often has less resources, less support and less clear motivation (including the expectations of others – clients and colleagues alike) to enable her to persist in the counselling skills role than those who have more formally constituted counselling roles. Until her skills and understanding are well established and she is confident of her value in using them it will be easier to fall back on her first and more usual construction of her client's difficulties and the prescriptions and directives that follow from this.

When the helper remains doubtful about her ability to initiate or sustain a counselling skills response despite the apparent need for such help, there are two possible ways forward for herself and her client: either to refer or consult with others. In the first case it is good practice to explain the difficulty to him and to discuss the possibility of finding another source of help. Such help may be within either statutory or voluntary agencies; may be specialist in providing for people identified by type of problem (for example, bereavement, breakdown of relationship, drug abuse); may identify itself as acting for particular groups of people (for example, the elderly, single parents, ethnic minority groups); may offer one-to-one counselling, group support, advice or other forms of more directive help (for example, Relate (Marriage Guidance), British Pregnancy Advisory Service and Cruse offer individual counselling in most parts of the country, while many single parent groups offer support and resources in proportion to the larger numbers involved). Cities and larger towns often publish directories of helping agencies. Sheffield Information Service, for example, publishes a 400-page guide to community organisations and services, titled *Help Yourself*. In the absence of such a publication, the local library will probably carry a similar list of such organisations. It is preferable that the helper makes a contact beforehand with the agencies she may use so that she knows both individuals and procedures within them and has some confidence in their capacity to help a particular individual when the need arises. Again, an agency may be more receptive to one of her clients if it has knowledge of and some feeling for the source of referral.

It was stated above that the referral should be discussed with the client. This is important to ensure that the client understands what such a move means for him. For example the helper might say: 'I have given some thought to what was said at our last meeting and I don't think I will be able to help you. However there are two other more experienced people that I believe would be more use – would you like to discuss the possibility of your talking to them?'

A second option for the helper faced with doubts about her ability to cope with a particular client is to continue to work with him in the belief that sufficient support and help is available to inform, enable, and sustain her through a difficult period. Support may be available within the profession or agency. Often, most typically in health care, it is not. The single most important source of support for helpers is systematic supervision. This is increasingly being adopted by the helping professions, although nursing and teaching so far have only a limited form of this which is mainly management-orientated and is called appraisal. The important topic of supervision will be discussed more fully in Chapter 6. It is enough to say here that the practice of regular consultation with a skilled and knowledgeable other person offers a means of help both to the client and the helper; it also offers opportunities for the achievement of personal and professional growth and learning within the work role.

What is our contract?

Among counsellors, contracting is seen as an essential part of the counselling process. It sets up and maintains the conditions for the counselling; it establishes boundaries and thus provides containment and security for both parties; it determines a framework within which counselling can take place; it offers, through control of time, place, cost and intention a useful emphasis on the value of these things and creates a purposive climate for the work to take place in.

By contrast our professional helper who is not designated as a counsellor probably has control over fewer of these variables and to a lesser extent in any case. She may not be seen by her client to be offering a counselling attitude; the place in which she works or from which she visits the home functions for a purpose which is not explicitly counselling; the 'normal' time for her business with her client may not provide for the extended conversation that her use of counselling skills often requires; and finally, as we have seen, her purpose in adopting a counselling attitude may, initially at least, be at variance with her client's expectations of her. It is understandable and may be appropriate in these circumstances that she avoids direct reference to contractual items already stated. She may feel it will disconcert the client or perhaps unnecessarily dramatise or over-formalise the personal or intimate discussion her client is now engaged in.

Despite this it is still necessary in using counselling skills to work towards a clearly identified contract as soon as possible. The counselling session, whether it bears that title or not, will benefit from agreements about when, where, for what purpose and in broad terms how things are to be carried out. It is also important, if it seems that the work will extend over a number of sessions, to set out the frequency and possible total number required. Within that period the helper and client will together check on their progress towards whatever purpose was originally agreed between them. To illustrate some of this, here is our school teacher, Stephanie, arranging her first meeting with Mark:

Stephanie: I think we ought to go somewhere more private to talk about this – let's see if the medical room is free – all right?

Mark: Yes.

(in the medical room)

Stephanie: Now, let's see. . . . I've got fifty minutes before

> I'm due to teach this afternoon, but I need twenty minutes for my lunch. How long have you got?
>
> *Mark:* I don't mind, but Mr Wallis wants to see me as well, at 1.45. I've had my sandwiches already.
>
> *Stephanie:* Good. Then what do you say to us having thirty minutes together now and then arranging another meeting for later in the week if we need to?
>
> *Mark:* That's all right for me.

Part of a helper's reluctance to engage in this sort of contracting process or a more explicit definition of her counselling skills role may be related to her own insecurity in this way of working. Many of us are reluctant to state our purpose until we are reasonably confident in achieving some positive result. Counselling, even for the most experienced practitioners, is particularly difficult in this respect, because except in the most general terms we are not sure of what the result is going to be. If the helper's work ethic or environment is more directed toward objective change in her client (as in a 'medical model' of health or a behavioural approach to education) then it is probably less sympathetic to her use of counselling skills than to helping in more objective ways. Despite these initial difficulties, however, with increasing self-awareness in the counselling skills relationship of her own motives and abilities, with an understanding of the usefulness of each stage of her development of counselling skills (a 'stage' model will be presented in the next chapter) and with good use of supervision, her confidence and purposeful contracting of herself in this way will undoubtedly grow to the mutual advantage of both her and her client.

How is it going?

'How is it going?' is a question that counsellors and counselling skill users should frequently ask. The ancillary questions in Figure 6 (Am I coping? How do I feel? How well did I do? What am I expecting of myself? Have I managed time appropriately? Does my client feel I have helped him?) all point to the need to monitor the counselling skills process, both in the helper's and the client's interests. To some extent this monitoring process can be achieved by regularly checking with the client how things are for him – by a review or reconsideration of what has happened. Again, it is important to avoid the leading question. 'How do you feel about this session/talk/meeting?' etc. is preferable to 'Have you found this session helpful?' But the helper herself has the means of monitoring the session both during and after the event itself. With experience she will be able to recall and reflect on the conversation with her client and learn from this (see pp. 100–1 in Chapter 6). Probably the most significant answers to these questions, though, will come from the process of supervision, which is also more fully discussed in the next chapter.

DISCUSSION ISSUES

1 Use Figure 6 on page 77 to consider your own future or past response to a situation in which you judge(d) it appropriate to use counselling skills. In what ways do you see your responding as satisfactory? Where are there difficulties? How can these be alleviated?

2 To what extent is counselling or the use of counselling skills recognised by your employer and/or your manager as part of your work? What benefits or losses do you experience from this situation?

3 What are the limits to confidentiality in your place of work? What could your client reasonably expect you to keep to yourself? How would you deal with circumstances where it is impossible to maintain confidentiality?

6

The Developing Helper

HOW DO WE DEVELOP OUR COUNSELLING SKILLS?

This question refers to two processes: one describes the individual learning – the growth of competency and understanding in the use of counselling skills; the other identifies the means of learning, the people who help the learner to learn. It will be helpful to look at the first of these to see what is generally true of the individual development of counselling skills so that such development may then be observed or sought in the relationships with influential others.

THE INDIVIDUAL LEARNING PROCESS

How, then, do we move from the state of being unaware, unknowing and unskilled in the context of our counselling work with clients to a position of knowing who we are, what we are doing and how we are doing this within the counselling skills process? How do we get to feel confident in our skills, more secure in our understanding of what is happening both to us and to our clients as well as more positive in our management of the process itself?

Two descriptions of this learning process usefully identify stages and levels of competence so that both learner and teacher can see what progress has been made. These are called the Competency Model and the Additive Model.

The Competency Model

The idea that the acquisition of skills follows a pattern that progresses from unawareness of one's lack of skill to the integration of skills into a higher-level monitoring of the counselling process is neatly encompassed in a four-stage description attributed to Robinson (1974: 538–9). This proposes that one moves through three changes from the initial (unconscious incompetence) to the final (unconscious competence) stages as shown in Figure 7.

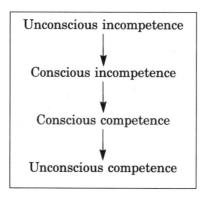

Figure 7   The Competency Model

We will now examine these stages and the changes between them in more detail.

Unconscious incompetence to conscious incompetence

The description of the first stage or starting place for development refers to those who do not know what counselling is about and are not able to use or demonstrate counselling skills. Furthermore they are unaware of their own ignorance or inability in these respects. Even this lack of ability and awareness hides two rather different starting points for the counselling skills learner; these positions might be described as the 'uninformed' and the 'mistaken'. The uninformed are those who simply do not know what counselling is or how it is conducted. They may never have given any consideration to its method or content or, because they have had no training or practical experience of it, they judge it to be a matter of common sense or simply a rational sorting out of a problem.

The 'mistaken' actually comprise relatively large numbers of professional helpers (like Jan whom I referred to on pp. 1–2) who, in using their own professionally acquired skills of giving support, instruction, advice and information, believe they are undertaking counselling in the sense that I have tried to use the word throughout this book. In fact they are often using their own previously acquired professional frame, trying to assimilate their client's problems within it, to find ways of alleviating the difficulty or solving the problem; in this mode the helper uses her authority, her understanding and her expertise to bring about changes in or for the client, instead of working to enable the client to understand and begin to achieve his own internal and external changes. In saying this I do not want to imply a judgement about the efficacy of working in an authoritative way; I am simply pointing out that it is not out of the counselling stable. The use of one or another approach with a particular client is always a matter for the professional judgement of the practitioner and her special knowledge of her client.

To begin to move to a position of 'conscious incompetence', that is, to realise that counselling entails more than or is of a different quality from one's present beliefs or practice, therefore, is a major step. It is to recognise the differences stated above, and implied through this book, between helper-centred and client-centred attitudes; to see that the verbal and non-verbal skills themselves both support and promote client autonomy; it is to believe in the ability of the client, the deeply rooted capacity within himself to grow and change; and to understand that, in order to enable her client to achieve this growth the helper has at least temporarily to abandon her own authoritative approach and all of her previously hard-earned knowledge of her client's condition and how that may be improved.

In coming to understand this the helper reaches the state of conscious incompetence, for although she now knows what to do she also discovers that she can't actually do it. The understanding of the principle of client-centredness, for example, is one thing; to maintain a client-centred stance in practice with a client or a trainee colleague is much harder to achieve. Again, to know something *about* the basic skills of paraphrasing, reflecting feelings, asking open questions, etc., immediately faces one with the knowledge that their apt and fluent use in the communication of the client's experience is, at that point, not accessible.

Conscious incompetence to conscious competence

In practice some experienced helpers who are beginning to use counselling skills within their work find it difficult to abandon their more authoritative style, even for a brief period. They understandably want to maintain their existing competent interpersonal skills in preference to a clumsy and less fluent use of counselling skills. They may hope instead to integrate the newer attitudes and skills into their existing approach in a more piecemeal fashion.

I am not sure that this works. From my experience in working with many groups of people who are in this position I am led to believe that a more total change of attitude, a new outlook, as it were, is desirable as soon as the differences are understood, notwithstanding the feelings of incompetence and even helplessness that this may invoke. Once the learner understands that a new direction or a change of hats – use whatever metaphor you will – is required, it is probably better to begin to travel this road, however slowly or unsurely, with some intention and awareness of what is or is not being achieved. Clearly this implies a determination to stay with the client's account of things by whatever means, including, perhaps, a fairly obvious repetition of client statements and a committed use of silence in preference to meeting social convention by introducing irrelevant items. Skill acquisition is a slow process requiring attention to specifics (i.e., particular verbal skills) in the early stages while the more general view of what is happening is only partly encompassed. Later on, the interpersonal skills are less closely monitored when the helper's attention turns more fully to the client himself, the relationship and the direction of the counselling skills process.

The integration of skills into the larger view of the helper–client interaction is achieved by practice – either in the training or working situation – and the vital feedback that is obtained from those sources. We shall see in more detail how this is to be achieved later in this chapter. In the meantime our learner is beginning to understand from her experience that even the deliberate and very conscious use of counselling skills with her clients is effective. They can make use of this kind of intervention even though she herself lacks confidence. The skills themselves communicate empathy, which is an integral part of a new and more productive relationship. She is moving into the last phase of this sequence of developing competency.

Conscious competency to unconscious competency

Are you a car driver? If so, which foot do you use for the clutch, which for the accelerator and which for the brake? If you have to think about it or even have resort to trying your feet out on some imaginary pedals in front of you then your driving skills are at a level of unconscious competence. The actual conscious control of those pedals, which as a learner you struggled so hard to achieve and accurately co-ordinate, has long since been relegated to an almost automatic function so that it goes unnoticed in the day-to-day business of driving. So it is with communication skills in general and gradually with counselling skills as a special example of these. At this level the helper does not normally notice whether she is paraphrasing or questioning, nor does she make any conscious decision to use these or any other verbal skills as such. In fact they become part of the more conscious processes of understanding the client, unpacking the detail, noticing particular feelings, confronting the unspoken and so on. And in their turn, even these strategies become, in her experience, absorbed by the growing picture of her client as a whole person, functioning well or less well as she understands him.

The benefit of this relegation to the helper's unconscious control lies in the freedom she then has to observe and monitor broadly what is going on, or to choose to focus very specifically on one event or another, if that seems to be significant. Also of course the freedom from more deliberate use of skills as such means that she is able to be her more authentic self in the counselling relationship, thus providing another of the core conditions for client change (see p. 42). A further option also exists, which is once again, this time more deliberately, to attend to her employment and execution of specific skills. Such a choice would be useful in the development of herself and her abilities if it were to establish more effective methods of facilitating her client, for example, in using questioning less or silences more.

In considering the Competency Model we are faced with the idea of growing competence and decreasing incompetence. While it does not explicitly establish a failure to meet clients' needs at stages prior to that of unconscious competence (and I have explained why I think good use can be made of skills at the conscious competence level), there are nonetheless implications that success equates with a completed journey along this particular road. Because this is less than the whole story, I want to present another way of looking at counselling skills development which identifies more positively what can be achieved with clients almost from the outset of any learning about the counselling skills process. I call this the Additive Model.

The Additive Model

As it happens, the order in which we considered the basic skills of counselling in Chapter 2 also has significance for the learning and practice of counselling skills in the work of the professional helper. Thus:

1 Listening
2 Communicating understanding
3 Challenging

One learns first to listen in a person-centred way, then to articulate one's sense of this to the client and finally one gains the means of sensitively confronting the client's experience. Each of these strategies depends on the understanding and application of that or those previous to it. There is a logical order for the process of development.

More important than this, though, is that each successive level of response provides in itself significant therapy for the client. I am arguing here for the helper's committed and confident use of a counselling response with her clients throughout her learning of these strategies. At whatever point she may be in developing her counselling skills she can offer a useful service to the client, i.e., listening (and little else except to support the conversation) is of value. Secondly, the addition of 'communicating understanding' importantly extends the scope of the counselling skills process and the helper–client relationship, but these two levels of response still have a completeness of intention and scope reflecting the theory of a person-centred approach. Thirdly, challenging skills add further dimensions to the helper's strategies when properly built on and integrated with the previous two. Because much has already been written of the importance of each of these as part of the effective counselling skills process (again, see Chapter 2) there is no need to reiterate that information here. However it remains still to justify their position in a developmental scheme where each in turn is seen as having this additive or 'bolt-on' function.

Listening

Listening, therefore, has therapeutic value (p. 15), although in practice it is not usually appropriate to maintain total silence. It is also necessary to use 'minimal encouragers' such as nods, 'uh-huh's, etc., as well as supportive conversation indicating concern and interest in order to sustain both the listening process and the implied social contract established by taking such a role with a needy other person. Nevertheless listening is a first-stage activity that is relatively easy to learn, is widely used as a means of releasing pent-up feelings or unloading problems and is an excellent precursor in fostering a client-centred attitude for the later stages where the counsellor is to be more active. Listening is a strategy that is identified by several agencies, including both befriending services and telephone helplines, as a prime means of responding to client need. It is also popularly accepted as an important way of offering support to another person, although part of this perception may also connect with the fact of giving time to and being physically in the company of that person.

Communicating understanding

The next and appreciably more difficult achievement is to communicate this understanding, predominantly in words.

However it is in this more interactive process that the therapeutic relationship is built and, as I have already explained (p. 17), the client becomes better understood to both parties. In achieving this we have both the necessary and sufficient conditions for client change, for it is in exactly this and little more than this that Rogers places his claim for the client to achieve significant personal changes (1961: 38). Of course, there is a wide range of opportunities for the communication of understanding to take place and to some extent this range does beg the ability of the helper in using them. To restate what has just been spoken is at one end of such a continuum of respondings; perhaps accurately and uniquely to name some key aspect of the client's experience when he himself is failing or struggling to do this, is at the other end. Both help to move forward the process of revealing and coming to terms with the client's own self, freeing him to make choices and move his life in the direction he wants it to go. As the helper begins more fully to take on the client-centred attitude so she is better able to relate to what she is understanding and in turn sensitively and accurately to express this understanding for both herself and her client to work with.

Challenging

Little more needs to be said. If we now take on the challenging skills the possibility exists to help the client forward more quickly, since, by definition, these involve the presentation of material outside of his present experience. The actual skills and the conditions under which they are employed are described on pages 24–34. The appropriate use of these offers a further dimension of helper activity which, like the second-stage activity of communicating understanding both extends and yet integrally depends on the previous stage(s).

DEVELOPMENTAL AGENCIES

Having considered two accounts of how counselling skills users may grow in themselves and their abilities, let us now turn to some sources of such growth and learning which are available to the helper. The four that I want to discuss are supervision, training, clients and self and the helper's employing organisation. They collectively represent the idea that counselling in general is distinguished from many other professional cultures by its interest in the continued monitoring of and provision for the worker's good practice, her psychological security, personal growth and professional development. This process is achieved by reference in the first instance to some form of supervision.

Supervision

The *Code of Ethics and Practice for Counsellors*, written and published by the British Association for Counselling (1990: 6) states that 'it is a breach of the ethical requirement for counsellors to practise without regular counselling supervision/consultative support'. Supervision is referred to as 'a formal arrangement which enables counsellors to discuss their counselling regularly with one or more people who have an understanding of counselling ... and supervision'. It also sees the purpose of supervision as: 'to ensure the efficacy of the counsellor–client relationship', and advises that the counselling supervision should be independent of the line manager role. Obviously many helpers already work within a code of ethics which applies to their primary professional practice. Many do not provide for supervision, most notably the large professions of teaching and nursing. However, it is clear that where any helper is regularly using counselling skills in the way that this book has described that process, then she also requires supervision in the same way and for the same reasons that designated counsellors normally receive it.

However, the adoption of supervision for helpers whose work involves the use of counselling skills is far from being general practice. In some areas, social work for example, the practice of supervision is better established, although its adequacy for a worker who is spending substantial amounts of time using counselling skills may again be in question. In other areas, for example in residential care, supervision is in its infancy but is growing; again this may serve the agencies' purposes in general, but is unlikely to provide the counselling skills user with proper support.

Though all supervision is primarily aimed at benefiting the client, this is achieved by means of three main functions: personal support for the worker; worker education and development around the work role; and the pursuit of good practice within the work itself. All of these can also be seen to offer opportunities for development. As Gaie Houston reports in her imaginative and entertaining book, *Supervision and Counselling* (1990: 1), her supervisee, when asked what she was expecting from supervision, replied 'I really want SUPER vision', i.e., a 'god-like overview' of what is going on. What counselling skills users should (also!) expect from their supervision is a better understanding of their clients, but also of their own personal and professional selves, of the interaction between their clients and themselves and of the supervision process and how to use it. What the helper expects or needs from her supervision, though, also depends on her own level of experience, maturity and understanding in her work. Hawkins and Shohet (1989: 48–53) describe a developmental approach to supervision which proposes four stages of supervisee development, each implying a different kind of attitude in the supervisor, as follows:

Stage 1: Self-centred
- dependent on supervisor
- lacking criteria for self-assessment
- difficulty in seeing the broad picture or identifying main features of process

Supervisor has to give guidance and direction, feedback and support.

Stage 2: Client-centred
- over-confident versus overwhelmed
- identification with versus isolation from client
- begins to appreciate complexity of process
- resistance, anger, challenge to supervisor

Supervisor may need to give 'parenting' or emotional holding.

Stage 3: Process-centred
- fully present with client
- has overview of process
- has overview of the relationship

Supervisor, now more of a colleague, uses discussion and confrontation.

Stage 4: Process seen in wider context
- work seen in a wider context
- wise, articulate
- autonomous

Supervisor may be of a different theoretical orientation to supervisee.

Training and learning resources

One of the benefits of being in counselling or therapy oneself is in coming to have an intimate and very personal understanding of the process. One can trust it or believe in it both for oneself and for others. On a training course we rely on the knowledge and experience of the leader or training staff for this assurance. Courses themselves should aim to provide understanding of the theory and practice of the counselling skills process as well as opportunities for the development of competence in sustaining and managing the process itself. They should also enable members to become more self-aware in the counselling skills role so that they can argue for and work towards obtaining support and resources for good practice. Whether such courses are staged inside or outside the workplace they should offer participants the opportunity to consider their own work practice and to prepare, perhaps to plan and rehearse, alternative approaches, strategies and skills in work with their clients. There is not the space here to give detailed accounts of how such aims might be achieved, but some practical advice on how to obtain training in counselling skills may be helpful to the reader.

1 The British Association for Counselling produces several publications about training. The two most relevant are *Training in Counselling and Psychotherapy* (Chaytor 1992) which is a comprehensive list of courses throughout the UK, and *In-house and Tailor-made Counselling Skills Training* (Chaytor and Palmer 1992) which is a directory of members offering this type of training.
2 Many local Higher and Adult Education Services offer day and evening courses in counselling or counselling-related areas, including counselling skills. These are often oversubscribed and an early application is advisable.

3   The two most popular journals, *Counselling*, published by the British Association for Counselling, and *Counselling News*, published by Central Magazines Ltd, regularly contain advertisements for counselling courses of all descriptions. Many professional weekly and monthly publications also inform readers of courses in counselling skills relating to their professional interests and backgrounds.

4   Finally the British Association for Counselling may be approached for help with training or development in counselling. It lists among its aims to: 'provide support for counsellors, particularly opportunities for their personal growth, education and training.' One significant way in which this aim is achieved is through its annual conference, which usually offers a wide choice of workshops, talks and experiential sessions over a two-day period as well as the opportunity to meet others working in counselling or related areas.

Among the training resources I would also include books and tape recordings. A list of recommended books is included at the end of this chapter.

Learning from clients and self

Clients are a rich source of learning and professional development. As has already been explained we can only begin to understand our clients if we adopt an empathic attitude. We have to learn what it is like to be them and in doing this we have also temporarily to put our own worldview on one side. Our clients tell us if we are successful in doing this by their responses to what we say and do. We can judge the effect of our interventions by the use that clients make of them – in our use of self-disclosure, for example. We can also explicitly check with our client both about how and by what means we are successful. Such a reviewing process is important for both parties and may be undertaken briefly during or at the end of a session or, more extensively, over a full session put aside for that purpose.

Casement (1985: 29f.) usefully develops the idea of an *internal* supervisor which derives from the helper's experience of supervision, her own therapy, and monitoring of and reflection on both the counselling and supervision processes. Though this concept is more fully developed than I can explain here it is comparable to some of the awarenesses of stages 3 and 4 in the developmental approach to supervision described earlier (pp. 98–9). It invokes the image of what Hawkins and Shohet call 'helicopter skills'. In using these or in referring to our internal supervisor we are somehow establishing the means of taking a separated view of ourself in the helping role, of our client and of the relationship between the two; it also implies the facility of zooming in to inspect one of these more closely whilst the others recede from view. Casement presents several fascinating accounts of how, using his internal supervisor between sessions, he was able to put himself in his client's shoes and gain crucial understanding of his client's enigmatic or uncooperative behaviour.

The worker's organisation or agency as a source of her development

The fourth and final means of developing counselling skills is through the worker's own employing agency or work-related organisation. This exists in the first instance to provide an optimum service to its clients and to achieve this has to ensure that its workers themselves function as well as possible, which in turn is achieved only by attending to staff development. The latter includes supervision and training which have already been discussed as an essential means of a worker's development in her use of counselling skills. The point of this section, though, is that the agency through its policies and day-to-day management *has control* of the means of its workers' development in all contexts and can promote or neglect these as it determines. This implies attention to all of the functions included here, which, in addition to supervision and training also means the provision of policy, resources and an organis-ational climate which is supportive of the use of counselling skills with clients or co-workers. The use of counselling skills in the workplace requires both facilities and time – it is not a cheap management option and it is important to assess its worth both to clients and staff. Staff will not be able to show such benefits, however, unless management also shows com-mitment to this form of good practice, designing and implementing policies that clearly state its intentions to use and support counselling skills in the work of their staff, offering both moral and practical support in so doing.

CONCLUSION

The counselling culture is growing rapidly in this country. More institutions and organisations are employing counsellors and others who have training in counselling skills. I have tried, in this book, to anticipate the increasing volume of trainees and the demands they will make on the various training systems; I have also endeavoured to present what I feel is a realistic model of counselling for these learners, including space for individual growth and development within that; I have also argued for the provison of appropriately supportive conditions for the learning and practice of counselling skills, despite the fact that such conditions may not always be obtained, due to lack of understanding or resources. Nevertheless I believe that these and the levels of skill, understanding and self-awareness described here are what we should expect in others and strive for in ourselves, whether we be managers, employers, administrators, colleagues, helpers or any others whose concern is to provide the best possible service to a person who is sometimes in need.

DISCUSSION ISSUES

1 Does the Competency Model reflect your own experience of learning any kind of social or interpersonal skill? At what stage of competence do you judge yourself to be in your development of counselling skills?

2 What experience do you have (if any) that simply listening is of therapeutic value?

3 'Supervision is a management tool to get more work from already over-worked staff' and 'Supervision is useless because my manager usually tries to avoid it – so I don't bother to push for it either' are two somewhat negative views of supervision. Do you agree? How do you visualise getting more out of supervision for yourself? How important is it that you have non-managerial supervision for your counselling work?

4   What are your plans for development of the counselling aspects of your work and your own abilities, awareness and understanding in this?

Further Reading

Culley, Sue (1991), *Integrative Counselling Skills in Action*, London: Sage. Focuses on the skills of counselling (with plenty of examples) built into a three-stage model. A purposeful and practical work.

Jacobs, Michael (1988), *Psychodynamic Counselling in Action*, London: Sage. A thoughtful and entertaining introduction to psychodynamic counselling, including two extended case studies.

Mearns, Dave and Thorne, Brian (1988), *Person-centred Counselling in Action*, London: Sage. This provides a clear explanation and practical illustration of Carl Rogers' person-centred approach to counselling.

Nelson-Jones, Richard (1983), *Practical Counselling Skills*, London: Holt, Rinehart & Winston. An introductory text with explanations and exercises – includes discussion of cognitive and behavioural approaches.

Rowan, John (1983), *The Reality Game*, London: Routledge & Kegan Paul. A broader look at humanistic counselling, its theory and practice.

References

CHAPTER 1

British Association for Counselling (1969), Steering committee of the standing committee for the advancement of counselling, proceedings.

Dryden, W., Charles-Edwards, D. and Woolfe, R. (1989), *Handbook of Counselling in Britain*, London: Tavistock/Routledge.

Russell, J., Dexter, G. and Bond, T. (1992), *Differentiation Project – Summary Report*, The Advice, Guidance and Counselling Lead Body Secretariat, c/o Julie Janes Associates: Welwyn.

CHAPTER 2

Culley, S. (1991), *Integrative Counselling Skills in Action*, London: Sage.

Egan, G. (1975), *The Skilled Helper*, Monterey, CA: Brooks/Cole.

Nelson-Jones, R. (1983), *Practical Counselling Skills*, London: Holt, Rinehart & Winston.

Rogers, C. R. (1980), *A Way of Being*, Boston: Houghton Mifflin.

Roget (1966), *Thesaurus*, Harmondsworth: Penguin.

Stewart, I. and Joines, V. S. (1987), *TA Today*, Nottingham: Lifespace Publishing.

CHAPTER 3

Ellis, A. and Dryden, W. (1987), *The Practice of Rational-Emotive Therapy*, New York: Springer.

Glasser, W. (1965), *Reality Therapy*, New York: Harper & Row.

Kopp, S. (1972), *If You Meet Buddha on the Road, Kill Him!*, London: Sheldon Press.

Nelson-Jones, R. (1983), *Practical Counselling Skills*, London: Holt, Rinehart & Winston.

Rogers, C. (1961), *On Becoming a Person*, London: Constable.

References

CHAPTER 4

Burnard, P. (1989), *Counselling Skills for Health Professionals*, London: Chapman & Hall.
Hawkins, P. and Shohet, R. (1989), *Supervision in the Helping Professions*, Milton Keynes: Open University Press.
Laing, R.D. (1970), *Knots*, Harmondsworth: Penguin.
Luft, J. and Ingham, H. (1955), *The Johari Window: A Graphic Model for Interpersonal Relationships*, Los Angeles: University of California at Los Angeles, Extension Office, Western Training Laboratory.
Rowan, J. (1983), *The Reality Game*, London: Routledge & Kegan Paul.

CHAPTER 5

British Association for Counselling (1989), *Code of Ethics and Practice for Counselling Skills*, Rugby: BAC.
British Association for Counselling (1990), *Code of Ethics and Practice for Counsellors*, Rugby: BAC.
Heron, J. (1986), *Six Category Intervention Analysis*, Guildford: University of Surrey.
Pratt, J. W. and Mason, A. (1984), 'The meaning of touch in care practice', *Social Science and Medicine*, vol. 18, no. 12: 1081–8.
Reddy, M. (1987), *The Manager's Guide to Counselling at Work*, Leicester: British Psychologcial Society.

CHAPTER 6

British Association for Counselling (1990), *Code of Ethics and Practice for Counsellors*, Rugby: BAC.
Casement, P. (1985), *On Learning from the Patient*, London: Tavistock/Routledge.
Chaytor, D. (ed) (1992), *Training in Counselling and Psychotherapy*, Rugby: BAC.
—— and Palmer, I. (eds) (1992), *In-house and Tailor-made Counselling Skills Training*, Rugby: BAC.
Hawkins, P. and Shohet, R. (1989), *Supervision in the Helping Professions*, Milton Keynes: Open University Press.
Houston, G. (1990), *Supervision and Counselling*, London: The Rochester Foundation.
Reddy, M. (1987), *The Manager's Guide to Counselling at Work*, Leicester: British Psychological Society.
Robinson, W. L. (1974), 'Conscious competency – the mark of a competent instructor', *Personnel Journal*, vol. 53: 538–9.
Rogers, C. (1961), *On Becoming a Person*, London: Constable.

Index

Index

Index

loss 42

managing the counselling skills process 64–88
monitoring the process 87–8
mother love 59
mutual understanding 76

negative self-image 61
nervousness 20–1
new perspectives 34
non-verbal communication: of client 14; of helper 13; posture, orientation, etc. 14
nurse 27ff., 67

objectivity 58
offer of counselling 78
open questions 22–4
opening dialogue 79
opportunities for use of counselling skills 70
organisation 101–2

paraphrasing 11, 15–18
parents 33, 44
personal growth 40, 62
person-centred theory 39, 40–4
planning action and change 34, 50
policy 101–2
potential 41–2
positive transference 33
prejudice 60
privacy 70, 71, 74–5
problem-solving 50
psychodynamic theory 39, 40, 44

questions 11; action 35, 50; closed, leading, why 23; open 35, 50

Rational-emotive therapy (RET) 47–9
Reality therapy 47
'receiving' skills 9, 12
referring client 84
reflecting content, feelings 16
reframing 24
reinforcement 49
rehabilitation nurse 69
relationship, helper–client 25

residential care 17; social worker 68
resources 101
respect 42–4
restrict information 74
Rogers 15, 30, 37, 39, 40–4, 58, 61, 76
role conflict 64–8; stress 55
Rowan 60, 61

safety 71
self-actualisation 62
self-advocacy 50
self as instrument 52; as physical object 63
self-assessment 37–8
self-awareness 52–63; growth of 60–2, 87; of client 24
self-disclosure 27–8
self-enhancement, fulfilment 42
self-indulgence 54
self-respect 48
sexual abuse 73
'shoulds' 48
skills, mental and verbal 8; understanding, challenging, action 10
social skills 7–8; worker 41–9
subjective experience 41
summarising 11, 18, 19
supervisee development 98–9
supervision 73, 85
supervisor 74, 97–9
support 85, 97; worker 67
sympathy 43

'talk time' 70
tea, coffee, offering 76
teacher 68, 72
teaching 4, 71
team leader 67
telephone 75
themes 28–9
theory 38; and practice 38–51
time management 5, 8, 79–80
thinking 58; and feeling 57–60
touch 69–70
training 101; and learning resources 99–100; in counselling skills 68

109